# PRACTICAL PROCESS IMPROVEMENT

# PRACTICAL PROCESS IMPROVEMENT

*A Program for Market Leadership in the Twenty-First Century*

R. Edward Zunich

SPC Press
Knoxville, Tennessee

SPC Press
5908 Toole Drive, Suite C
Knoxville, Tennessee 37919
(865) 584–5005
Fax (865) 588–9440
www.spcpress.com

ISBN 0–945320–65–5

*xii* + 170 pages

1 2 3 4 5 6 7 8 9 0

# Contents

# About the Author

R. Edward Zunich has been active in the field of industrial quality, productivity, and customer satisfaction for over 15 years. He developed the Practical Process Improvement (*PPI*) program based on experience with various quality systems during that time.

As a Navy Captain Ed Zunich commanded three combat ships and a major Navy base. In his final tour of duty he was responsible for implementing Total Quality Leadership throughout the Atlantic Fleet, some 250,000 people.

After retiring from the Navy Mr. Zunich served as the Vice President for Total Quality at Grimes Aerospace, where he successfully helped the company return to profitability. Since that time he has worked as an independent consultant and trainer. His clients include companies in such diverse lines as airfield lighting, inventory management and control, marking tags and labels, metal forging, and precision measurement and control.

He has a B.S. in Public Administration and an M.A. in Business Administration. He was an examiner for the Malcolm Baldrige National Quality Award and a member of The Conference Board Quality Councils Two and Five. He lives in Hendersonville, North Carolina.

Mr. Zunich first began developing his Practical Process Improvement program in 1994. He has trained hundreds of teams and thousands of individuals in the *PPI* program. Their successes have proven the effectiveness of *PPI*.

# Acknowledgments

The Author gratefully acknowledges the following people who helped both with this book and with the Practical Process Improvement Program.

I would like to give special thanks to Roger Jacobson. He has provided invaluable assistance in formulating and refining the Practical Process Improvement program over the years. Roger also read an early version of this work and provided valuable inputs including the Foreword. Tas Pinther, Jason Stone, Greg Wallender, and Dave Crowell also read an early version of this book and provided valuable suggestions and clarifications. Michele Combs has been instrumental in the development of the *PPI* program.

I would like to especially thank Dr. Donald J. Wheeler for insight and guidance regarding the technical accuracy of this work and for providing the Appendix to clarify some of the statistical concepts that are discussed herein.

Finally, I would like to thank my wife Norma for her patience, forbearance, and assistance with editing.

# Preface

This is a book about profit and market leadership. For simplification and ease of understanding the contents are written with an eye toward industrial enterprises. This is not to the exclusion of other enterprises and organizations. The principles apply universally.

Even though some enterprises are not for profit, and others are not industrial in nature, all organizations have certain aspects in common, among which is the need for an enduring stream of revenue that exceeds expenditures. In industrial applications we call this profit. In other applications different terminology may be used. But, the principle is the same. Without more revenue than expenses organizations are short-lived.

It will not require imagination to apply the principles in this book to non-industrial and not-for-profit applications. They work in service, educational, medical, government, and military organizations. It may, however, require some new ways of viewing and thinking about the problems and challenges that face us.

These principles have been employed in diverse applications with good success. The principles of a guiding aim and supporting metrics have been employed in a community church. Service organizations, such as medical facilities, have found great value in the concepts of customer focus and process improvement.

In the last decade the U.S. Military employed the concept of customer focus; going from a service-centric model to a customer-centric model. In many cases the individual services (Army, Navy, Marines, Air Force, and Coast Guard) sub-optimized their individual processes in order to optimize the ability of their customers (the Theater and Unified Commanders) to deploy and employ armed force to greatest advantage. This is an excellent example of application of some of the principles discussed in this book.

So, even though we use the industrial enterprise model readers in all occupations and organizations should find value in the contents of this book. Profit may be defined differently in non-industrial applications but focusing on the customer and reducing waste and costs are universally good things to do because they will help you stay in existence.

# Foreword

A transition of change, affecting us all, has been at work since we took our first breath. When comparing today's business environment to a year ago, change is evident. However, we only need to look in the rearview mirror a few months back to note the continual change in our business environment, and to see that the pace of change is steadily ramping up, stressing every functional work process found in any enterprise.

The world is emerging from fragmented to global markets with a geographical shift in where we find consumer, industrial and technological power players. Today's change is presenting a complex problem for any company just to survive, let alone profitably grow. Only those who are able to be extremely focused, agile and willing to fight for customer allegiance will compete with today's global competitors with shifting resource advantages.

This environment will continue to challenge business leadership and management to increase means to improve quality, speed of work and provide customer value proposition linkages in order to achieve a higher order of satisfaction feeding the lifeline of business.

Our ability to not only survive, but profitably grow requires business leaders to master the art of leading change and establishing a continual improvement culture within the organization. While the future may seem daunting, this doesn't require a complex mix of new methods, tools or advanced culture of humanoid species to navigate through the challenges of today and tomorrow. What will be required is a proven scientific method of continual improvement, a clear articulation by management as to where the company is going, how it will get there and what this offers each employee to cultivate a common aim and set of goals for the enterprise.

In this book Ed Zunich has distilled many years of research of various continual improvement methodologies, observation of the psychology of human reaction to change and hands on successful experiences. The methods presented in Practical Process Improvement (*PPI*) provide the secret to success for world class business performance. Ed illuminates the elements that make the difference between winning and dropping out of the competitive race.

I have had the pleasure of working with Ed for over a decade in implementing Practical Process Improvement in companies engaged in the aerospace, semiconductor, life sciences and industrial market segments. While each market has its unique requirements and challenges, implementing *PPI* has been universally instrumental in driving a rapid turnaround in performance improvement. What I have found to be the underpinning for this success involves three commitments from management.

1. First and foremost, management must personally be *involved*. Achieving success is too important to risk delegating the lead of continual improvement activities.

2. Management must lead the charge to be focused on customer satisfaction. We are talking energized organizational focus and enterprise passion for responsiveness and quality to provide customers the products and services that offer the highest value the customer can obtain.

3. Management must allow employees to take ownership of their work processes and engage employees in the decision making process at the lowest levels possible to improve speed of work execution and quality of work output.

In personally leading, implementing continual improvement and working within the *PPI* environment I have seen organizational teams tackle a broad range of improvement projects. *PPI* Teams have achieved cycle time and quality defect reduction improvements as high as 70% and easily in the 40 to 50% range. The results have not been limited to product production and engineering processes, but also include administrative, finance, human resources processes and the commercial efforts of marketing and sales. This type of improvement, coupled with a focus on customer needs has gained many significant financial advantages for the enterprise.

In this book, Ed outlines the system of improvement; addresses human behavior and the psychology of dealing with change; discusses the importance of metrics as well as understanding and controlling process variation. The application of *PPI* provides the discipline for when and how to take proper action for problem root cause solutions.

You will find elegance in *PPI* offering a methodology that at one end of the spectrum is simple and practical to allow every employee methods to improve their work, while remaining open–ended in embracing sophisticated improvement tools should the problem be extremely complex.

*PPI* offers a blended continual improvement methodology to equip you and your organization to advance enterprise performance, deal with changes the competitive world presents and lead change your competitors will be required to contend with as you refine the art of doing business in your market space.

Roger Jacobson
Vice President, Global Operations
Thermo Electron Corporation

# Chapter One

# Introduction to Practical Process Improvement

Practical Process Improvement is a simple approach to making money by involving everyone in the enterprise. There is a common objective: *to boost profit* by practical application of proven methods.

Practical Process Improvement operates on two paths simultaneously. First, *PPI* accrues savings from waste reduction and process improvement. Second, *PPI* grows revenue through innovation and a focus on quality and customer satisfaction. *PPI* leverages the combined effect of cost savings and increasing revenue to accelerate profitable growth. *PPI* does not rely on an anointed cadre of experts to do these things. Everyone in the enterprise is employed in the effort, using simple logic and straight forward methods and tools.

The current fad is to use an improvement model to determine a "sigma" level for products and services. But, faith in this fad is misplaced.

- The model is inwardly focused on process reengineering to the exclusion of innovation.
- The model actually has no statistical validity; it is little more than arithmetic gone astray. (We will discuss this in more detail in Chapter Two.)
- The model leads to a false sense of security as we will see in the following example.

Take the case of the quality of a printed circuit board. On a modern, complex board we have a great number of components, variables, and attributes. We may define 10,000 or more things that could go wrong. Using the "sigma" model these things are defined as *opportunities for defect*. The logic is extended to *defects per million opportunities*, or *DPMO* and a corresponding "sigma" quality level.

So if a single board component, or a solder joint, or a polarity, or a voltage measurement causes one board in fifty to fail we extend the logic as follows: one defect in fifty boards, with 10,000 opportunities per board, calculates to one defect in 50,000 opportunities, or 20 defects per million—*20 DPMO is almost "Six Sigma" quality level*. Not bad, but for one small detail. We did not ship the customer a million boards. We probably only shipped him a few. The customer simply sees a defective board that costs him time and money to deal with.

Which way of looking at the problem is correct? It depends on whether you are an anointed member of a cadre of experts attempting to improve your numbers or if you are the customer stuck with the bad circuit board.

Practitioners of the "sigma" model seem to be perpetually trying to outdo each other with new, complex statistical and mathematical ways of dealing with problems. They set up controlled experiments following the philosophy that the same conditions will always produce the same results. They gather data to the smallest detail, perform complicated statistical operations, and produce answers that do not work. Why? The truth is that the same conditions do not always produce the same results. Nature does not work that way. This is difficult to accept so our practitioners devise methods that do produce consistent, acceptable answers.

Their answers may be consistent, but consistency and correctness are different matters entirely. A smart person once told us, "If we torture the data long enough it always surrenders."

In the Nineteenth Century an American industry emerged that has become part of the fiber of our culture—patent medicines. Still prevalent today, they were rampant then. The difference now is that the Pure Food and Drug act cured what was called "The Great American Fraud."

During the horse and wagon era, peddlers were notorious, pulling their medicine shows from town to town to peddle their product. The elixirs, tonics, and other cures had little healing value. But the peddlers went to great length to legitimize their product. Some were ex-preachers and most employed tactics linking their product to temperance and benevolence. The larger traveling shows employed advance men and fanfare. Many employed assistants, dressed as men of the cloth, to circulate through the audience with an air of morale rightness in their endorsement.

Over time the worthless remedies came to be known as "snake oil." We are not sure how the name came about but the term has become synonymous with a quack remedy. A major component of most snake oil remedies was alcohol. The tonics were sipped with a wink. The alcohol's effect often explained the euphoric effect of the placebo.

Today we are seeing another form of snake oil—statistical snake oil. The peddlers make their point with fanfare, advance men, and testimonials. The arguments are no less intoxicating than the tonics of the past, and no more effective. Unfortunately, statistical snake oil is not regulated. There is no "pure statistics law" to regulate its development or use.

Practical Process Improvement avoids statistical snake oil. *PPI* does not establish pompous preconditions and rules to find answers we like. *PPI* deals with the world as it is. We cannot always predict what the answer will be. We cannot predict if the answer will be favorable or unfavorable. We can only deal with data in a rational manner and then deal with the results from logical analysis of that data. Often the most reasonable possibilities (common sense) turn out to be wrong.

*PPI* does not rely on common sense. *PPI* relies on giving people the ability to experiment and accept the results. And, most importantly, *PPI* gives people credit for having the intelligence to interpret the results and take appropriate action. Prejudices and biases are the enemy of ingenuity, innovation, and progress. If progress is to be made it is necessary to accept things as they are without some preconceived notions of how they ought to be.

*PPI* does not deal in fact, for there is no such thing as a fact. It is not possible to prove what we know; it is only possible to understand what we do not know. For example: we can visit the corner bookstore and buy a book titled *North Carolina Atlas & Gazetteer.* This book states that Badin Lake has an area of 5,350 acres. Is this a fact? Well, we would have to ask the following questions.

1. How was it measured?
2. When was it measured?
3. What features were included in the measurement?

Change the answer to any of those questions and you will get a different number. If you measure the lake in August the water level may be lower than in June. If you include the area up to the high water mark the number will be different than if you include only the area at mean level. If you physically measure the various dimensions the number will different than if you calculate the area using a sampling model. It is not possible to "prove" that the area of Badin Lake is 5,350 acres. It is only possible to understand the limitations on our estimate and the approximate accuracy of the number. The number 5,350 acres is a data point, not a fact.

*PPI* deals with data. The most important aspect of working with data is retaining the *context* of the data. Said differently, nothing in the way the data is presented should lead us to make a decision different from one we would make by examining the data in a simple, rational manner. Manipulating numbers to behave in a certain way or give us a certain result is no justification for the techniques employed. It is snake oil.

Let's return to our circuit board example. It is possible to define thousands of opportunities for failure on each board. If a board fails it is therefore possible to define a defect rate in terms of DPMO and make the conversion to some "sigma" level of quality. This sort of analysis masks the real situation; that is, the circuit board failed. We may choose to see it in terms of failures per million and feel good we got 99.998 % of it right. The customer, on the other hand, sees one failure per one circuit board—100% failure of that board.

*PPI* looks for solutions to problems logically and simply. First, we look for a solution from simple analysis of the available data. If necessary we gather additional data to form a solution. Then we test the solution and examine the consequences. We compare the result to what we expected, make adjustments as necessary, and then move forward. If the result is good then we can move on and continue to monitor the situation over time to ensure that we continue to get favorable results.

It does not matter how elegant the experiment is or how sophisticated the statistical technique is. The result must withstand rigorous testing against appropriate criteria. Even if the result is consistent with our desires we cannot automatically assume it is right. Remember, the same circumstances may not produce the same result next time. We can only continue to monitor the situation, making improvements along the way to ensure that our efforts keep leading us to where we want to be.

*PPI* establishes a logical and consistent framework for improvement. This framework is encapsulated in a succinct set of guidelines, the objective of which is optimization, customer satisfaction, and sustained profitable growth. (A discussion of these guidelines lies ahead in Chapter Five.)

*PPI* is not about guessing and hoping for miracles. *PPI* employs simple straight forward analytical techniques to *efficiently and quickly* derive a logical solution. We do not spend excessive time torturing the data. We do spend whatever time is necessary to ensure the results are justified and repeatable within reasonable parameters. We define the problem, analyze the data, develop solutions, and then test the results with great rigor. The key to progress over time is monitoring the results over time, not assuming things will simply chug along as we want them to. *PPI* requires discipline and persistence.

One of the ways of stifling innovation is to do what I call a return on investment (*ROI*) determination in advance of improvement efforts. This occurs when we only undertake projects in the area where we know, or think we know before hand, that the results will justify the effort. In using *ROI* predetermination the manager's project selection criterion is one thing only, correcting financial shortfalls—not innovation and not customer satisfaction. These managers only allow improvement efforts to proceed if it can be determined ahead of time that some financial goal will be met. This approach will ensure that many important potential projects will be left undone. ROI predetermination is snake oil. There are better ways to select projects.

ROI predetermination will usually ensure one other thing. The results you get will suboptimize the output of the enterprise. People will give you the numbers you want, but at what expense elsewhere? Usually, the improved numbers will represent only isolated gains. These gains are often achieved at the expense of another part of the enterprise and rarely consider the needs of the customer. The gains rarely come from innovation for innovation is too risky. This is especially true if people are rewarded monetarily for achieving the financial goal. Beware what you ask for, you will probably get it.

The objective of *PPI* is profit. As such, we employ appropriate techniques to select high impact projects focused on customer satisfaction. We do not stifle innovation by only focusing on saving money. We do not predetermine the financial impact; we measure it as it is after the project has been completed. Most projects attain significant financial savings, some do not. We accept the results as they are and unceasingly work to achieve the desired goal, customer satisfaction.

*PPI* assumes we live in an uncertain world. We allow people to say such things as, "I don't know the answer to that question. We haven't developed our processes far enough to know." We allow people to try things even though they might fail. For if we fail we then know how not to do it. We assume that people are intelligent and innovative and will do the right thing given the opportunity.

*PPI* assumes that our current processes are operating to perfection—that is, they are operating at the perfect level for giving us the results we are currently getting. If we want different results we need to make some changes. These changes do not always involve reengineering or process modification. Often, we only need to conduct training to reduce variation in our work—operate the process as it was designed without individual interpretation. We also assume that even if our results are good today they will probably not be good enough tomorrow. Global competition will see to that. Customers will demand more tomorrow than they do today. The forces of entropy are working against us. Status quo is not good enough.

## *What is Practical Process Improvement?*

Practical Process Improvement is a team based program for improving profit. *PPI* engages employee teams to improve all enterprise processes: production, finance, human resources, planning, sales, engineering, supplier management, and all other processes in the enterprise value chain.

The challenge in creating the program was to condense multiple methods, principles, and theories into one practical, usable, adaptable program. It was important to do this by creating a framework for optimizing profit.

There have been many approaches and/or programs for improving quality and productivity over the years. It is possible to isolate programs from the following schools of thought: 1) industrial psychology and human resources development, 2) statistical methods, and 3) systems theory. Many disciplines emerged, each with their own set of rules. Using one set of rules we get one answer. Using a different set of rules we may get a different answer. One set of rules may satisfy certain criteria for success but not others. It has not been possible until *PPI* to find a program that incorporates appropriately all three schools of thought, prevents contradictory logic, and yields consistent answers. This was a preeminent goal in developing *PPI*.

For example, many models contain team building as a primary program objective. Team building is a noble goal (often referred to as the touchy-feely motive). Yet, studies have shown repeatedly that teams formed for this goal more often than not fail to achieve measurable results to the enterprise bottom line.

Further, if team building is our goal then we must believe that there is a shortfall currently in our people, that is, they are not able to work together effectively. Proponents are normally quick to assert, however, that people are not the problem. But they cannot have it both ways. Their programs are built on a premise that people must be the problem (they are not working together effectively).

*PPI* puts shortfalls and inconsistencies such as these to rest. To continue the example, we begin with the premise that people are not the problem. Problems arise from the interaction of forces within our processes. We know that teams work best when they have a common goal outside of the team itself. That goal is profit. While team excellence is a wonderful bonus, the focus is on profitability—improving customer satisfaction and the bottom line.

*PPI* is built upon a simple data-based approach. *PPI* then integrates practical application of basic quality improvement tools, simple and innovative methods, and modern psychological and learning models.

*PPI* employs straight forward strategies for success that minimize the opportunities for suboptimization. This requires alignment of all projects with enterprise goals and objectives. *PPI* requires that the leaders of the enterprise establish and deploy a simple, understandable "aim" for the organization. The operative element of the aim is a system of guiding metrics to establish priorities and track progress. All *PPI* activities are aligned to the organizational aim through the system of metrics, thereby eliminating guesswork as to where to devote our efforts.

Advanced adult learning and psychological models are utilized extensively in building the structure and framework for presenting the body of knowledge. The approach for delivering the package is small groups of employees tasked with improving processes, hence the *PPI* team. The result is a syllabus and program that is effective and practical in its application, regardless of the sophistication of the end user.

There are three principles of *PPI*: apply logical simplicity, use practical methods and tools, and involve everyone.

## *Apply Logical Simplicity*

*PPI* capitalizes on the sophistication and power of logically simple tools and proven techniques. Everyone is able to understand these tools and techniques and apply them in a meaningful way in teams and in individual daily work. Even though the basic *PPI* tools are simple the program is open ended at the top for application of more complex tools and methods when required.

Traditional quality control methods (very alive and well today) rely on the detection method of quality assurance. This method employs a system of screening inspections to sort good from bad.

### *The Principles of Practical Process Improvement*

1. Apply Logical Simplicity:
   As Albert Einstein once said, "Logical simplicity is the only path that leads to more profound knowledge." Simplicity is the cornerstone of *PPI* program effectiveness and translates to a key competitive advantage.
2. Use Practical Methods and Tools:
   Unless the methods and tools are practical and easy to use, their application, and resulting improvement, will be limited to that attainable by only a few "experts".
3. Involve Everyone:
   Improvement is everybody's job. Everyone in the enterprise should be engaged in meaningful improvement activities focused on customer satisfaction and improving profits.

The purpose of screening is to ensure that all product conforms to specifications either during the production process or prior to shipping. But, world class quality is more than 100% conforming product. Conformance only means that we have met the specifications. Specifications seldom accurately describe what the customer views as world class, rather, only what is the minimum acceptable. While screening inspections may cull out the unacceptable items it does not improve the quality of the acceptable items. The detection method assumes that there are costs associated with quality improvement. Products are priced based on these costs and a desired margin. The detection method of quality assurance is expensive and imperfect.

So, we have to do something different. We call this the prevention method. There are critical distinctions between the

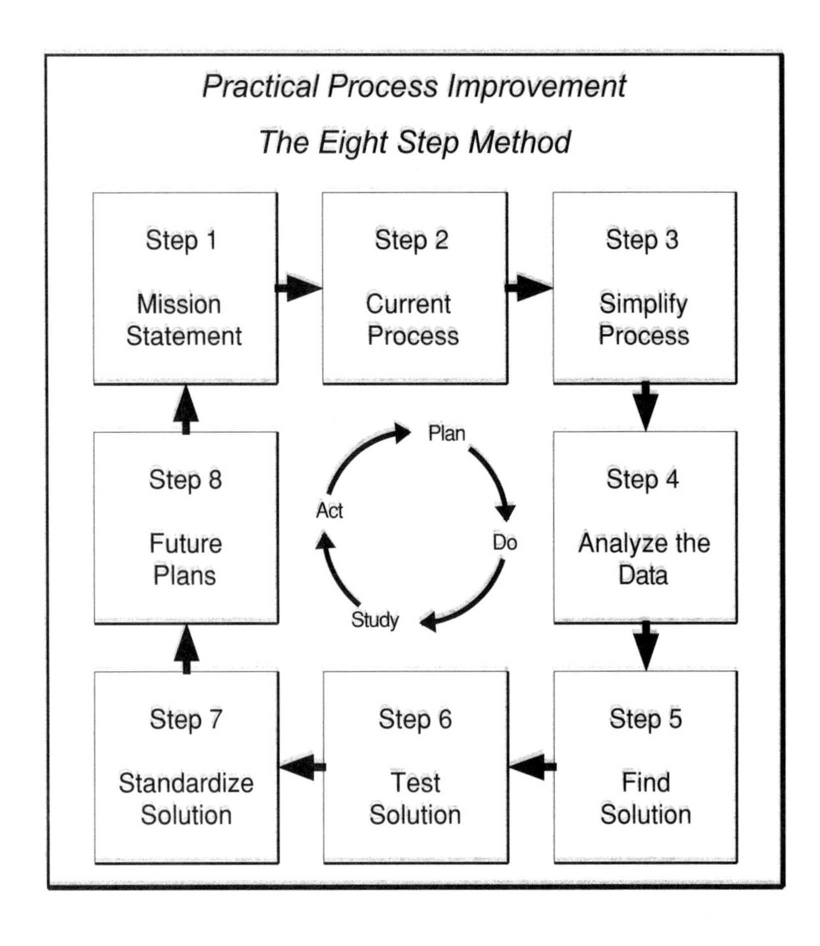


detection and the prevention methods. The prevention method is a logically simple approach to quality and customer satisfaction.

The basic premise is that quality may be improved while lowering production costs at the same time. Production costs are a function of our processes. If we improve our processes, we will lower our costs *and* increase quality and customer satisfaction. Product price is determined by the market. Higher customer satisfaction brings higher demand, more sales, and price flexibility. Price flexibility brings higher revenue and accelerated growth in profit.

## *Use Practical Methods and Tools*

*PPI* employs The Eight Step Method based on the Plan-Do-Study-Act model. The Eight Step Method emphasizes that learning is an iterative process, that discovery is a journey, and that meaningful improvement must be continual. The Eight Step Method is rigorous, requiring the appropriate use of data, analysis, and testing. Teams drive improvement and data drives team activities; not emotions, tribal knowledge, or past practices.

In developing *PPI* special attention was paid to the choice of tools to be used in improvement activities. It has been found that these tools fulfill the needs of nearly all improvement activities when used within the context of The Eight Step Method.

| *PPI Basic Tools* | *PPI Statistical Tools* |
| --- | --- |
| Meetings | Run charts |
| Brainstorming | Process Behavior Charts |
| Quick Vote | Histograms |
| Check Sheet | Scatter diagrams |
| Pareto Chart | |
| Flowcharts | |
| Fishbone Diagram | |
| Other tools as needed | |

## Involve Everyone

Another distinctive feature of *PPI* has to do with the relationship of people and quality. Traditional detection oriented quality methods have at their source the notion that people are the predominant source of quality problems. This manifests itself in many ways, often subtle. An example of the subtlety is the "team building" reason for employee project teams discussed earlier. It goes something like this, "Through teams employees will learn cooperation and other ways to prevent quality problems." The inference is that people are not cooperating now, ergo, people are the source of quality problems.

If, however, we think of quality as the result of resources transformed through processes into valuable goods and services, we may begin understanding the role of people in a different light. *PPI* views people as a resource. They are our only ubiquitous resource. As such, they are not the source of problems, rather they hold the key to profitability. *PPI* taps this resource, values the input, and puts it to immediate use in the organization.

Think of it another way. The human brain weighs about three pounds. So, if a manager is making all of the decisions he has three pounds of brains at work. But, if he allows his 10 employees to engage their brains as well as their hands he has thirty-three pounds of brains at work. Most enlightened managers fully understand the potential in their people.

Within *PPI* the managers' role has changed from decision making and directing to training, teaching, and implementing improvement solutions identified by teams and individuals. This is a key difference of *PPI* compared to other programs. Delegation is not an option. Management "buy in" is not enough. Management, under *PPI*, is integrally involved with specific duties, responsibilities, and objectives.

## *Summary*

There are two objectives for this book. First to bring together some ideas—some simple and commonly understood, some not so simple or commonly understood—in order to provide the framework and fundamentals of the *PPI* program. And second, to discuss these ideas in an orderly way to understand how they fit together as a system, not merely a collection.

It is assumed that you have a basic knowledge of the concepts of process and quality management. But, expert knowledge will not be required. Things will be explained as we go along.

The book is presented in two parts. Part One, consisting of Chapters Two through Six, which discuss the basis for managing within the PPI model—the PPI management method; and Part Two, consisting of Chapters Seven through Ten, which discuss the elements, training methods, and implementation of the *PPI* Program itself.

In addition to these two parts there is also an appendix entitled Avoiding Sigma Confusion. This appendix was prepared at my request by Dr. Donald J. Wheeler. The purpose of this appendix is to provide the clarification needed to help you avoid some common causes of confusion. I recommend that you read it before you read Parts One and Two.

Part One

# The *PPI* Management Method

# Chapter Two

## Customer Satisfaction

What is customer satisfaction? What is quality? Who defines quality and who actually determines the quality of a product or service? Why do we pay more for high quality products and services? These are all questions that, answered correctly, lead us to a definition of quality and customer satisfaction.

Over the years, several definitions of quality have been proposed. The most prevalent are:

1. conformance to specifications,
2. capability for intended use—form, fit, function, and
3. customer satisfaction.

The first two of these definitions, while concise and easy to measure, fall short under scrutiny. The third, customer satisfaction, is more comprehensive, but is seldom completely defined.

Practical Process Improvement adopts the notion that the quality of anything—an item, a service, an experience—is defined by customer satisfaction. We also believe it is possible to accurately define customer satisfaction in meaningful, measurable terms.

In my seminars, I conduct an exercise in which the question is asked, "Who determines the quality of an item, service, or experience?" The answer is invariably, "Why the customer—who else?"

This answer comes, I believe, from various quality and productivity improvement models from the past. It is an incorrect answer. While the customer judges the quality, the supplier is the one who actually determines the quality level.

Let's say it another way—we determine the quality of the products and services we produce. We do our best to meet customer desires. But, different customers have different desires. Desires change over time. Customer perceptions change over time. Customers judge quality based on their perceptions and desires at the time of purchase.

For example, the normal process for buying apples is to sort through the bin and pick out certain ones that suit our sense of a *good apple*. We did not determine the quality of the apples, the apple grower did. I doubt that any of us maintain a dialogue with the apple growers to ensure that we get the type of apple we want. On the contrary, the growers use marketing feedback to improve the apple growing process to the best of their ability. Once the apples reach the store shelves, however, all we as customers can do is judge whether or not the apples meet our needs.

How much are we willing to pay for the apples? In the past, this was in great part determined by the cost of production. The higher price resulted from the added costs of production and materials, added inspection, and stuff that was thrown away because it did not pass inspection. This is no longer the case. We are in a market-driven economy. The international market place determines the price of any good or service. The cost of production is increasingly irrelevant. *The market place determines the price tag, not the cost of production.*

Also in the past, there was a common misunderstanding that to improve quality, *using the detection approach* to quality assurance, we had to incur additional costs: production costs; material costs; and costs of inspection, scrapping, or reworking bad product. This notion is no longer appropriate. Practical Process Improvement applies the prevention approach to production in which costs are actually reduced as quality improves. This is a major shift of paradigm and a primary objective of Practical Process Improvement. Companies that do not understand this new paradigm will become increasingly non-competitive and will eventually go out of business.

So, it is possible to satisfy our customers through increased quality, while at the same time, we reduce the costs of our system of production. The profit equation is:

$$\text{Profit} = \text{Revenue} - \text{Costs}$$

Using Practical Process Improvement methods, costs are reduced as waste is eliminated, and production efficiencies are realized while quality is improved. Revenue growth comes from two phenomena:

1. we may be able to increase our price because of quality improvements, and/or
2. we may enjoy increased volume of sales from greater customer satisfaction.

Profit is a function of customer satisfaction. It comes from innovation and a relentless pursuit of quality. Is it possible to establish a general theory of customer satisfaction? Yes. Customer satisfaction may be defined within the structure of five basic elements, each of which is definable, quantifiable, and measurable. These elements of customer satisfaction provide a working model applicable to all situations. The five elements of customer satisfaction include: quality, availability, price, image, and anticipation. These will all be discussed below.

## Quality

In the context of Practical Process Improvement, quality is defined by such characteristics as form, fit, and function. Fitness for intended use is very important. Quality also includes intangibles: characteristics that are important to the customer but difficult (but not impossible) to define. We include in this dimension not only product quality, but as well, field sales and service, warranty, installation, and all other aspects associated with the product or service. The quality of services is also included in this definition of product quality.

It is tempting to think of such aspects as field sales and service as separate from product quality. But Practical Process Improvement defines it this way: *A perfect product needs no field sales or service. No warranty would be required if there was never a failure in the field. A perfect product would require no installation.*

Are these notions unrealistic? We do not think so. Today, it is possible to buy a computer over the Internet (no field sales), requiring no installation (it comes ready to use, plug and play), for which warranty is not an issue (price and quality obviate the need for an extensive warranty), and with no need for a field service organization (all service is handled on-line, by telephone, or in rare cases, by return to the factory).

It is also tempting to describe quality only in terms of specifications and other linear measures. However, customers do not judge quality by conformance to specifications. Rather, they view the quality of a product or service using subjective standards of judgment. They increasingly do not judge products to be *good* or *bad*. Whether the product could be measured and found in or out of specifications is increasingly less important than other factors.

Yes, it is true that some industrial customers do judge conformance to specifications, often because of legal requirements. But these customers invariably use other criteria as well. It is a mistake to believe, under any circumstance for any customer, that just because our product or service "meets the spec" that we have satisfied our customer.

Customers today use a continuum of criteria, usually derived from values, perceptions of the marketplace, or demands of downstream customers. Their judgment results in an understanding of overall quality, not a decision of good or bad based on comparison to fixed standards or specifications. Based on more than just specifications, customers judge a product to be within or below their threshold of perceived quality.

There is another problem—a trap—from relying solely on specifications. The trap is that merely measuring conformance to specifications tells little about the process that produced the product. Measuring to specifications may only lead to an invalid assumption that our process is okay when it is not. Managers may have a false sense of security. Invariably, the forces of entropy will lead to process decay and nonconforming product. The manager will have no idea of how the process got where it is. In reality, the quality of the product can be no better than the process of production.

There is a popular model for measuring quality, based on conformance to specifications, that utilizes a concept called *defects per million* (*DPM*). In this model, defects (or defectives) are counted for a sample population and then extended to a fraction per million. Unfortunately, the *DPM* definition of quality does not hold up under scrutiny: *DPM* is *never* correct unless the sample size itself approaches a million.

When using the *DPM* model, data is taken from the population of a product or event. The amount of data usually considered valid is a sample size of about 35. Conversion of data from a relatively small sample population to a fraction-per-million is inappropriate arithmetic with no foundation in statistics.

Think of it this way. When the sample size is large enough, such as "dropped telephone calls" per million attempts, no conversion is required; it is simply a count. In this case a count is valid because telephone companies really can count a million or more attempts. But for a smaller sample, we are only guessing when we extend it to a per million number. We have to assume that things will stay the same for a considerable time into the future. Unfortunately, nature does not work this way.

But even a large sample *DPM* tells us little about the process; that is, it does not tell us "why" the event(s) occurred. All we know is that there was, or is, a problem. We do not know when in the process of production it occurred. And more importantly, we do not know if it will occur again. We do not know if it is a result of one cause or multiple causes. We can only guess at corrective action. (Practical Process Improvement uses tools and methods that do help us determine these things.)

There are other problems with the *DPM* model, as well.* Dr. Donald J. Wheeler points out four problems with *DPM*.

---

* A more complete discussion of *DPM, DPMO,* and the Six Sigma conversion may be found in Dr. Wheeler's book: *Guide to Data Analysis*, SPC Press, Knoxville.

1. *DPM is incomplete.* It focuses only on the costs of scrap and rework. It does not include the costs experienced by the customer.

2. *Defects-per-million computations convert straightforward count data inappropriately. DPM* computations extrapolate from a relatively small sample to a universe of a million. This is equivalent to raising an assumption to the third or fourth power. A conversion that may be appropriate for a parts-per-hundred computation is not appropriate for a part-per-million inference.

3. *DPM computations assume that a process will not shift more than 1.5 standard deviations in either direction from some avreage value.* When a process is shifting around it is unpredictable, and there is no limit on the size of the shifts that can occur. This means that rather than trusting in the *DPM* assumption, in practice, an efficient mechanism will be needed to monitor the process location.

4. *Converting parts-per-million nonconforming values in reverse in order to define a "sigma-level" for a process, is nothing more than torturing the data—making snake oil.* This practice uses a descriptive statistic for a small population (a count of defects or defectives) to make a predictive statement about a universe of potential events (the defect-per-million assumption) without the benefit of performing any analysis. Further, it ignores the reality that some processes are predictable and others are not.

Another closely related calculation is *defects per million opportunities* or *DPMO*. In this model we extend the "per million" calculation to an assumption about the number of opportunities for the defect or defective. For a better understanding of *DPMO*, let's once again look at our earlier example (from the Introduction) of the quality of a printed circuit board.

We may have as many as 10,000 opportunities for defect on a typical board. The logic is extended to defects per million opportunities, or *DPMO*. One defect per 10,000 opportunities per board, in fifty boards, calculates to one defect in 50,000 opportunities, or 20 defects per million. But what if our batch size were 100? Then our calculation would result in 10 defects per million—a better number. When people are exposed to the opportunity to make things look better through arithmetic, they often find the temptation irresistible. *DPMO* is totally subjective and lends itself to manipulating the data until we get a number we like—torturing the data until it surrenders. More snake oil. But wait, there's more.

Once you get a *DPMO* number that you like, it is still not a measure of quality. *DPMO* is a calculation of yield from the production process. It tells you nothing about either the quality of the product or how it meets customer requirements. The author of a recent article in a prominent magazine quoted a statistic that the *DPMO* for aircraft carrier landings was about 13. As an ex-Naval officer, this gave me pause. First, every successful launch results in a landing; *successful* is a matter of definition. Second, a successful landing is expected, not a measure of quality. Finally, quality is determined from measurements between the launch and the landing in answers to questions like: Was the ordinance delivered on time and on target? Did the sortie arrive on station on time? Were hostile air targets engaged successfully? A successful landing is not a measure of quality.

Dr. Wheeler states it succinctly. "As a result of these kinds of problems, any of the *DPM* values can only be characterized as a triumph of computation over logic. The *DPMO* is a totally subjective value that depends upon how you subdivide the continuum into potential opportunities. It is nothing more than data divided by an assumption."

*DPMO* and its conversion to a corresponding "sigma-level" has an alluring charm, but it is a placebo. The charm is that we can use arithmetic to say we have reached some level of quality even though we have no knowledge about our process or the customer's assessment of our product. Practical Process Improvement avoids this alluring charm by focusing on quality as seen by the customer. Quality is improved by understanding the processes of production and by taking appropriate action based on the situation. Improvement is an iterative process. Processes will not "run" unattended; they need to be managed. The primary statistical tool to understand and manage our processes is the process behavior chart. It is the only tool that will consistently and reliably provide the necessary information to manage our processes correctly.* It is the most effective tool to improve quality as seen by the customer. (We will discuss the process behavior chart in the next chapter.)

When we focus externally on the customer, instead of inter-

* The process behavior chart was invented by Dr. Walter Shewhart at the beginning of the Twentieth Century. This tool is alternatively referred to as the control chart. The names are interchangeable, however, the term process behavior chart is more descriptive and will be used herein.

nally on our sigma level, there is one more benefit, and it is huge. The path to market leadership is through innovation. Innovation results from viewing our products and services as the customer sees them. The innovative spirit is inseparable from a learning environment. Our ability to learn and innovate is our most powerful competitive advantage.

## Availability

In all sectors of today's marketplace, on-time delivery is increasingly important. Time is the essence of today's successful enterprise.

As consumers, we are deluged with buying opportunities. Our fulfillment horizons are very near. *We want it when we want it.* If the desired product is not available, there are plenty of alternatives. We have been taught, through experience, that we should not have to wait. This is true in all markets: retail, industrial, research, service, profit, not for profit—all markets.

Additionally, as we shall discuss later, modern concepts of productivity put new meaning on the old saying, "Time is Money." Time is more than money. Time is the truest measure of waste in a system of production. Time is a robber of profits.

Therefore, on-time delivery may be the most crucial of the five dimensions of customer satisfaction. Demands for quicker delivery are unceasing, placing great demands on manufacturers and their supply chains. This is creating a ripple effect that is causing the pressures to accelerate. Faster and faster performance is and will be required.

Express shipping is a method often used to speed up delivery. But methods such as this are at best interim measures, and they are costly. While we used to be able to pass costs such as this on to our customers, many sophisticated customers today actually penalize suppliers who only meet delivery goals through express shipments or other costly methods. Coupled with the requirement to reduce delivery time, price reductions are also expected over time. And, we are expected to continually increase the quality of our product or service. Quality, costs, and delivery time must all be improved to stay competitive. On-time delivery demands, however, may be our most significant challenge.

## Price

In the past, price was related directly to production costs. Suppliers marked their prices based on material, labor costs, and profit margin. Quality was determined by the quality of materials and workmanship in the product and also the amount of inspection, scrap, and rework. Inventory expense, processing expense, and other overhead costs were passed on to the customer as *a cost of doing business*. People assumed higher sticker price meant higher quality. *You get what you pay for* was the mentality. This is no longer the standard expectation.

Price, in the current economy, has little if anything to do with production cost. Price is simply the market price: what the customer is willing to pay. The market price is derived from the cumulative customer perceptions of value, considering all five elements of customer satisfaction. The value determination is subjective. Customers apply subjective standards during a purchase based on their perceptions of the product compared to other similar ones. Market price is a function of customers' judgment against their subjective standards. Costs of production are seldom a consideration.

If there is an invisible hand directing the economics of the market place today, it is determining the market price of a product or service without consideration of costs of production. The cost of production is becoming increasingly meaningless to our customers. That is why it is so important to continually remove waste and cost in order to remain competitive. Moreover, when we improve quality, it simultaneously increases customer perceived value, allowing us greater pricing flexibility.

## Image

Closely related to price, image reflects past performance and future promise of our products, our competitors' products, and the customers' perceptions of value. A good image is earned only through hard work and it is very fragile. Image is the culmination of our performance in the market place—the culmination of our customers' judgments.

Image is very important in the profit equation. Customers do willingly pay more for a product with a prestigious image, while a similar product with a different image, made by the same company, sells for less. It is important that we recognize this and capitalize on it with increased quality and availability. A better image gives us the ability to set our price at a desired level. We have the luxury of increasing price, if that is our strategy. And, because our efforts to increase quality and availability have resulted in lower internal costs, we may alternatively choose a strategy to lower costs and increase revenue through volume.

Image has a great impact, not only on profit, but on our ability to develop strategies that enhance our strengths and mitigate our weaknesses.

## Anticipation

The concept of anticipation is really very simple. It is defined as the customers' changing standards of judgment over time resulting from changes in products, alternatives, individual circumstances, and the marketplace itself. Future customer expectations are based on their past experience.

Anticipation is really an outgrowth of conditioning. Conditioned response results from repeated association with a condition (or stimulus). Customer anticipation results from repeated association with conditions in the market place, and it leads to future expectations. What are the conditions in the international market place today? What are the expectations for the future?

- Product quality issues of the past have been resolved. Things are expected to be basically free of defects. The quality of any item will improve over time.
- When demand exceeds supply, prices go up.
- When supply exceeds demand, prices go down.
- International competition results in ample supply, so there is no reason for prices to go up. To the contrary, prices are expected to go down over time as supply exceeds demand. (For example, think of flat panel televisions.)
- High quality may or may not accompany a large price tag. Price is determined by value, as judged by the customer. Specifications are only a measure of minimum requirements, not value.

- Customers are willing to pay more for a product because of its favorable image. They often believe their image will be improved by the product image. Image is an important factor in the customer's determination of value.

We are in an era of technological innovation. The pace of innovation has been accelerating and is expected to continue accelerating into the future.

The concept of anticipation incorporates the dimension of time into the customer satisfaction model. Customers anticipate that the conditions of the past will carry forward to the future. They anticipate improvement and expect that innovation will result in an accelerated tempo of change. Anticipation accounts for customers' increasing demands for more perceived value and lower price over time.

It is futile to attempt to maintain status quo; that leads only to failure. It is not enough to stay up with customer expectations, it is necessary to be out ahead of the customer. It is necessary to predict customer anticipation. Our ability to do this will likely determine the longevity of our enterprise.

The phenomenon of conditioning and anticipation has great significance in today's marketplace. Changes are more rapid now than ever in the past. The rate of change will accelerate—technology will see to that. An enterprise that is unable or unwilling to continually learn newer and better ways to satisfy its customers will not survive.

## Summary

The five elements of customer satisfaction are interdependent. That is, they come as a set, inseparable. A change in one results in changes to the remaining four. Therefore, it is probably not possible to isolate the results from a decision in just one dimension. All five elements extend to considerations for important business decisions. An understanding of these elements, and their interdependence, is necessary if we intend to optimize profit.

Simply playing games with numbers is not enough. Having good numbers may make us feel good, but it does not tell us how to improve for the future. Practical Process Improvement methods are designed to ensure that we analyze data within the framework of customer satisfaction.

Gathering and using meaningful data gets us into the game. Whether we win or lose depends on how we use the data—how we play the game. The game is played by everyone in the organization. All employees have a direct effect on outcomes. Senior executive activities clearly carry great weight. But, it is a mistake to believe that senior executives can win the game alone. It is more appropriate to understand the value of every employee and leverage that value for maximum enterprise effectiveness.

The bottom line is that we must delight our customers with higher quality products, better prices, with faster delivery and improved image, while remaining ahead of their expectations and our competitors' advances. People in a *PPI*-guided enterprise are able to directly affect enterprise success through an understanding of the customer and the elements of customer satisfaction. Enterprise success and longevity in great part depends on everyone's collective ability to satisfy customers now and in the future.

# Chapter Three

# Production Methods

Having discussed the dimensions and importance of customer satisfaction, we now turn to a discussion of ways to achieve customer satisfaction. We will examine two production methods that are prevalent in industry today: the detection method and the prevention method. You may conform to specifications using either method.

Using the *detection method*, improvement in conformance results from increasing the intensity of screening inspections—a procedure put in place to sort good from bad. One hundred percent conformance is achieved by improving the inspection standards and procedure to the point that nothing slips by. There are companies achieving very high levels of conformance using this method, but there are two problems with this method. First, detection may let you ship mostly conforming product, but it does *nothing* to improve the quality of any one item. Detection is focused only on conformity, not on the prevention of nonconformities. Second, screening inspections cost money, those costs increase with every refinement in the screening procedure. Costs of screening are in addition to the costs of scrap and rework—throwing away or fixing the entire pile of nonconforming product. The detection method is an expensive way of doing business.

The *prevention method*, on the other hand, aims to correct the source of poor quality by improving the processes of production. Inspections are not undertaken solely for correction or sorting. The primary purpose of inspection is to gather data that may allow us to make process improvements. In mature organizations, screening inspections are often eliminated entirely. The inspections shift from one hundred percent screening and the counting of defects to samples for measured data to ensure quality. Methods are available to maintain processes in a stable, predictable, and conforming state. When a process is in this state, a very small daily sample adequately represents the entire population of manufactured product. The efficiencies and cost savings are significant.

Using the detection method, quality improvements are accompanied by additional costs. These costs take the form of added inspections, added scrap, inventory, rework, and work in progress (WIP). The most grievous cost, however, is the added time that is put into the production processes. This results in longer customer lead times and dissatisfaction.* Conformity may be very high, but conformity is only one aspect of customer satisfaction. With the detection approach, the costs of achieving high conformity include higher production costs as well as lost revenue from declining customer satisfaction.

By using the prevention method, quality improvements are accompanied by lower costs and higher profit. Efficiencies take the form of fewer necessary inspections, lower scrap volumes, lower inventory, less rework, and cycle time reductions that equate directly to shorter customer lead times. Product quality improves

---

* Customer lead time would be more aptly renamed customer wait time.

continually. Costs are reduced continually. And an increase in quality and availability (shorter lead times) brings greater customer satisfaction. So profits are improved, not only by lower production costs, but also by an enhanced image and the revenue that image brings. This improvement in quality and customer satisfaction cannot be static. It has to be continualy renewed in order to meet the evolving requirements of the customer of the future.

### *Two Methods of Satisfying Customers*

| *Method* | *Characteristics* |
| --- | --- |
| Detection | • Specifications define conformity, not quality.<br>• There is a reliance on inspection to sort good product from bad.<br>• Increased conformity incurs additional cost from tighter specifications, more screenings, or both.<br>• Generally, people are considered to be a primary cause of poor quality. |
| Prevention | • Quality is improved by improving the processes of production.<br>• Poor quality is prevented by removing the causes from the processes of production.<br>• Processes of production include all enterprise processes, not only manufacturing processes.<br>• Quality is the result of the interaction of all resources of production.<br>• People are a resource, not a cause of poor quality. |

## The Detection Method

The detection method relies on specifications to define conformity. Screening inspection is the primary method for determining conformance to specifications. The purpose of a screening inspection is twofold: Screening during production (in-process screening inspections) are designed to "catch" defects early and correct them before they cause a product failure, while inspections at the end of production (output screening inspections) are designed to "sort" good product from bad product. When bad product is detected there are only two options: rework or scrap.

There are some problems associated with the detection method. Screening inspections simply catch defects or sort good from bad. No value is added to the product, only cost. We are, in effect, paying our workers twice: first to make the product and then again to correct defects. Screening inspections become more inefficient as the level of nonconformity decreases (example: airport security screenings). Specifications are the guideline used for screening inspections. But as we discussed earlier, specifications rarely define customer satisfaction. At best, specifications define minimum acceptable quality. In reality, as customers judge quality on many other factors, specifications are often not even a consideration.

The detection method implicitly assumes that every problem has a definite cause. The assumption behind the detection method is that the greatest variable is the worker. (Modern experience has shown this is not the case.) The purpose of screening before final inspection and packing is to find and correct problems, normally assumed to be caused by workers in the processes. Great effort is made to scientifically place the worker in the production processes in a way that minimizes their ability to create problems. Their work flow is measured, metered, and monitored. In modern day iterations, the worker is sometimes removed entirely and replaced by robots.

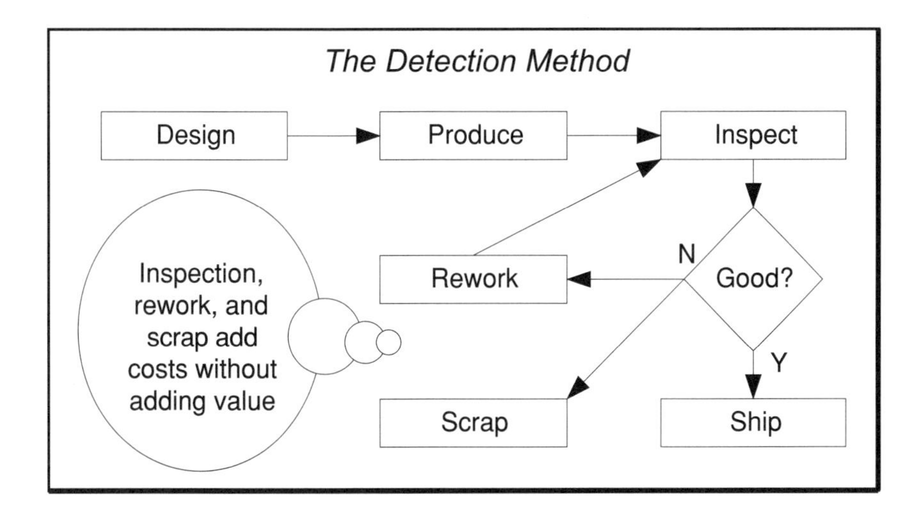


It is interesting to note that the detection method and the school of Scientific Management are very old. (Go/no-go gages were employed to detect problems over 140 years ago, and Frederick Taylor published *The Principles of Scientific Management* at the beginning of the Twentieth Century.) From the detection method came the management structure that is still predominant today. It is based on the underlying theory that people are the cause of production and quality problems and managers have to be installed to fulfill a policeman role. In this model workers are treated like machines. Over the years it has resulted in alienation and dissatisfaction. Workers checked their brains at the door—

they were not supposed to think, just do their jobs. While many progressive enterprises have actually moved beyond this model, many others think they have, but have not. They have put in matrix management schemes, a complex organizational structure, and they preach empowerment.* Their actual practices derive, however, from an underlying paradigm: People do not have the best interests of the enterprise at heart. So, we must *prod* and *manage* them accordingly.

When relying solely on inspection, problems are detected only after it is too late. The damage has been done. If the problem is correctable, it requires additional cost. If the problem is not correctable, there is no choice but to throw it in the scrap pile.

The detection method of quality assurance is a very expensive way of doing business. It is possible to achieve high levels of conformance using the detection method—simply throw away all the bad ones. If cost were not a consideration, this might be okay in some situations. But costs determine whether or not we stay in business. And of note, the biggest costs are not even measurable. The heaviest damage comes from the waste of human talent.

Using the detection method we generate the notion that quality is the job of the inspectors. We create quality assurance departments that become another mouth to feed—cost centers. "The customer? We don't deal with the customer." is the common parlance. Quality has a negative connotation. It is an expense, something that we have to overcome. We look for devious ways to

* To empower is to, literally, give authority to someone to act on your behalf, such as we would empower an attorney. For a manager to empower her people in the true sense, she would give them the authority to make decisions on her behalf. In practice, managers shy from this definition. Empowerment often means assignment of the dirty jobs.

get around the inspection process. We even find devious ways to use bad material, ignore or rationalize inspection results, and ship bad product as if it were good—but we would never admit it.

I find it ironic that very pompous production managers and quality control experts are the first to claim victory for avoiding the detection method. "We correct problems upstream. We have been improving our processes for over ten years." These are some of the boasts I have heard. And when I go out on the production floor what do I see? *Nothing but inspections* to sort good from bad. And then I look at their administrative processes. Somebody forgot to tell these experts that administrative functions also contain processes. It is an inspection-based production system from head to toe—a nightmare. It is true that most administrative processes are support processes and should never be optimized at the expense of a core process. But neither should they be ignored. They are commonly a primary source of variation and other problems in the core processes.

So let's look at the alternative, the prevention method. Let's look at how to eliminate this nightmare. Let's look at how to improve quality with an eye on the customer while we improve profit at the same time.

## The Prevention Method

The prevention method relies on the system of production, the resources of production, and the improvement of the processes involved. The system of production encompasses the entire enterprise, not just operations and the shop floor. All functions and departments contribute to the profit equation. The resources of production interact within production processes to determine the outputs. We improve quality and productivity by improving the system of production, using statistical methods.

In the early Twentieth Century the prevention method was developed as a way of economically controlling quality. The prevention method brings together the disciplines of statistics, engineering, and economics to create a holistic management system. The prevention method opens the door to a new and enlightened method of management—continual improvement.*

The Practical Process Improvement approach to prevention utilizes three basic principles. First, the quality of the output of the system comes from the processes of production. Quality is made upstream, not at the inspection point. Second, it is possible to measure and analyze quality and production processes through the use of very simple statistical methods. Third, it is possible to improve our processes by conscientious application of those same statistical methods to eliminate or control causes of variation.

The prevention method describes technically and accurately that it is the production process that produces the level of quality. Core processes, together with their support processes, form the system of production. We can improve quality, reduce costs, increase customer satisfaction, and increase profits all at the same time. When we remove the causes of poor quality from the

---

* The prevention method was developed on the heels of Scientific Management and the detection method. Frederick Taylor's Scientific Management was introduced in the first decade of the Twentieth Century. The prevention method and continual improvement concepts were introduced about 20 years later. By then it was too late. While the statistical and engineering methodologies of continual improvement were widely deployed, the management methods were not. Managers were already deeply seated in Scientific Management and the detection method. We still see conflicts in these methodologies when we attempt to employ the *new* method within the *old* management custom.

processes of production, we in turn improve our system of production. These improvements are accompanied by efficiency, greater productivity, and lower costs. The resulting improvement increases customer satisfaction and the revenue stream, improving profits by the combination of cost savings *and* increased revenue.

The system of production is formed around processes that employ five resources of production—the *4 Ms and an E.*[*]

*The Five Resources of Production*
(4 Ms and an E)

| *Resource* | *Application* |
|---|---|
| Manpower | People and their actions in the process |
| Machines | All machines including computer systems |
| Methods | All methods, documented and otherwise |
| Materials | Provided by suppliers in the value chain including internal suppliers |
| Environment | Composed of two sub-resources: Social environment, Physical and technical environment |

In the prevention method, we begin with an understanding that it is the system of production that determines the quality of the product or service. This system encompasses the entire value chain and may be broken down into individual processes. *PPI*

[*] There are several variations to this theme currently in practice. Some lists include "metrics" and others substitute "mother nature" for environment. There are others. It serves us well, however, to remember that these are resources, not simply variables. These resources *determine* our output, not simply measure it, affect it, or monitor it.

methods improve quality and productivity by improving these individual production processes only within the context of optimization of the entire system. Improvement takes the form of waste reduction, streamlining, and removing variation.

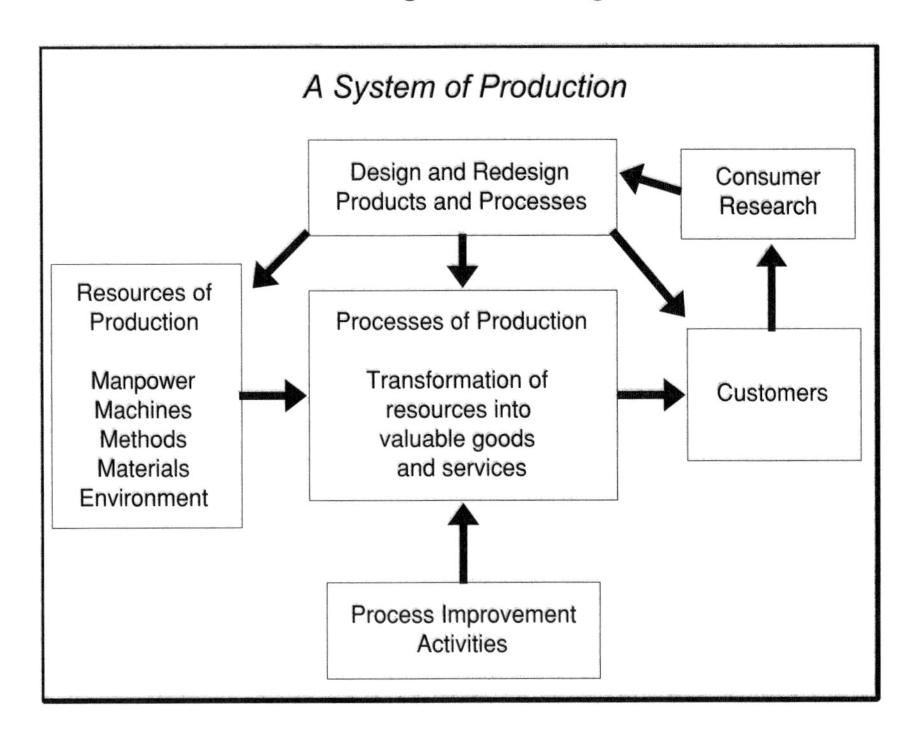


Our system of production is a closed system. Changes affecting any component within the system affect the entire system. Processes of production include all processes in our system—on the production floor, headquarters, and administration—all processes. It is not possible to optimize the system by optimizing every production process. Improving core processes is more critical than support processes. Support processes should never be optimized at the expense of a core process. But core processes must be optimized, even if at the expense of one or more support processes.

When we examine the prevention model, we understand that it is a mistake to try to cure quality and productivity problems without employing simple, valid statistical methods. Problems may arise from any of the resources of production individually, but usually from some combination and/or interaction of all of them. If we use some simple statistical tools we can make an initial determination about where to begin. Then, we may conduct an analytical study to determine the underlying cause or causes.

Sometimes, indications will tell us that the problem's source is isolated to just one resource or cause. If it comes from one resource, it is usually a simple matter to correct the problem. Other indications tell us when we cannot isolate the problem to only one cause. If a problem cannot be isolated to one resource then it must be some combination and/or interaction. However, if we do not use the appropriate statistical tools it is impossible to reliably make these determinations.

To jump to a conclusion without proper analysis will only make the situation worse. There is an exercise we conduct to illustrate why it is impossible to single out any one resource as the source of problems without the use of appropriate statistical methods. Look at the following equation:

$$A + B + C + D + E = 100$$

Now, solve the equation for A. Provide a specific number. You realize it cannot be done without more information, there are too many variables. So, every time there is a problem and we ask the question, "Who did it?" or make a machine adjustment or assume the incoming material is bad, we are solving the equation for only one variable. We will only make things worse. Why is this so?

There are five resources of production (remember the 4Ms and an E?). If we assume that one of these resources is the source of the problem, we are trying to solve the equation that we previously said could not be solved. There are too many variables. It is not possible to single out people, machines, or materials without knowing the values for the other variables. We must analyze our process and the interaction of the resources of production.

Practical Process Improvement recognizes that people are a resource in the process, not the cause of poor quality. People, in reality, are the only constant resource. They are the resource we can count on to correct the problems of poor quality. They hold the solution. People are the driving power of the *PPI* program.

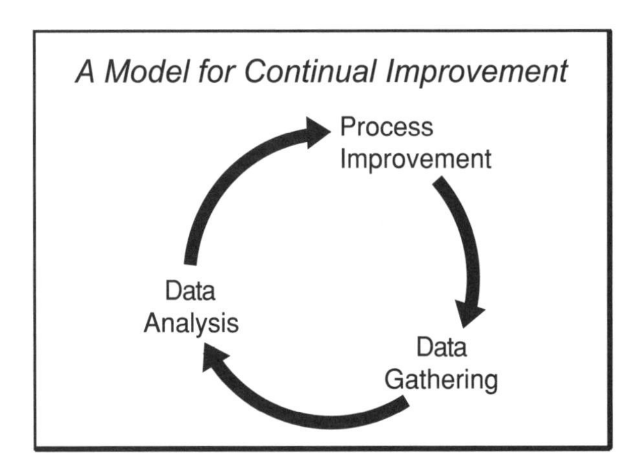


The prevention method also incorporates a model for continual improvement. Inspection is transformed into an orderly and meaningful way of data gathering so that we may analyze the cause or causes of the problem, trace those causes back into the process, and correct the problem at its source. Analysis is based on appropriate data, use of simple statistical methods, and appropriate study. *PPI* methods and tools are simple enough to allow everyone in the organization to participate in this analysis. We do not reserve these activities to the domain of a few experts, engineers, or managers.

In many programs, every problem is assumed to have a single cause; a root cause. This is accompanied by guesses as to what that root cause might be. By contrast, the Practical Process Improvement method of analysis begins with a statistical determination that allows us to isolate one resource or determine that it is some combination. The operational definition of the existence of a root cause is a signal—a point outside the limits of a process behavior chart. If there are no signals on the process behavior chart, then we can be reasonably sure our problem results from some combination of causes, not just one. A root cause methodology that does not begin with a statistical determination is not analysis, it is guessing.

Process improvement begins with the use of basic statistical tools to determine the level and type of variation in our processes. The primary tool is the process behavior chart. Process behavior charts measure variation in our processes. Variation is the cause of all poor quality. There are two types of variation, routine and exceptional. Routine variation gives evidence that our process is stable and predictable. Routine variation exhibits the effect of some combination of causes, none of which are apparent from the chart. There is no single cause that is evident. By convention, we call these causes *common*.

A Process Behavior Chart displaying routine variation is

shown below. Here the underlying process is subject only to the effects of common causes, and is therefore likely to be predictable in the future. A process displaying only *common* causes of variation results is a process with no points outside of the limits on a process behavior chart.

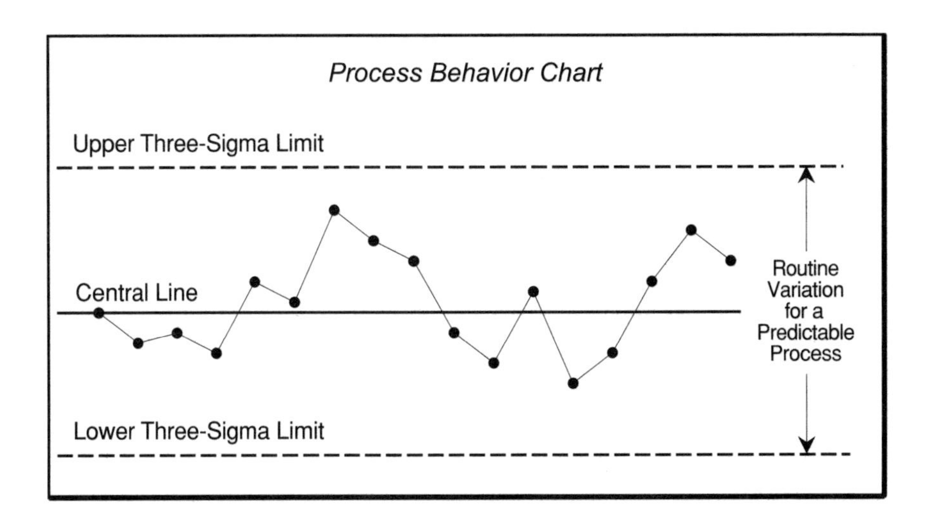


*Common* causes are inherent in the process. They are the result of the interaction of the resources of production. If a process exhibits the predictable behavior shown above, we are able to conclude that the observed variation is not attributable to any one resource, and we must analyze the process in greater detail to reduce the variation and improve the process. *Common* causes of variation are typical of a predictable, stable process that may only be improved by changing fundamentally the way the process operates.

The Process Behavior Chart shown below displays exceptional

variation, indicating that the underlying process is subject to the effects of *special* (assignable) causes and is likely to be unpredictable in the future.

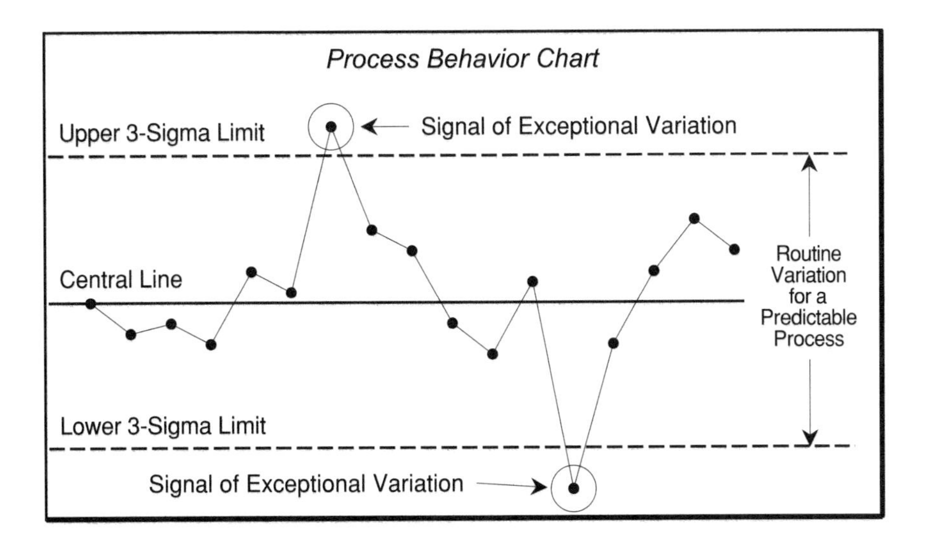


*Special* causes that result in exceptional variation will be indicated by a signal on the chart. These signals commonly take the form of a point outside of the limits. If a chart produces a signal, we are usually able to conclude that the signal points are attributable to one resource or cause. In this case our analysis is much easier: we need only isolate *that special* cause and fix it. *Special* causes are alternatively called *assignable* causes—because the exceptional variation may be assigned to one cause, not many.

When *special* causes are present, the unpredictability they create will make all discussion about future process outcomes uncertain—this is because we cannot predict when the special cause will influence our process again. So we have no way of knowing what an unpredictable process will produce tomorrow, or next week, or next month. While this is a problem, it is one that can be fixed—we can return our process to predictability by removing the effect of the *special* cause. But, there is no way to know if special causes are present or otherwise determine the condition of our process unless we use process behavior charts appropriately. Action taken in the absence of a process behavior chart is guessing.*

## Summary

The underlying methodology behind the *PPI* program is the prevention method. Simple statistical methods allow us to unlock the secrets of the processes of production, improve them, and thereby improve customer perceived quality as well as efficiency and productivity. Profit is improved by the joint action of lowering costs and improving revenue.

The strength of Practical Process Improvement lies in the value of people. We no longer rely on just a few experts to make all of the decisions. Now, people in the processes become the experts. They become the CEOs of their own jobs. We rely on them to think and provide them the authority to make decisions on quality, efficiency, and productivity. We engage the brains as well as the hands of everyone in the enterprise to increase profitability.

* More about the logic, construction, interpretation, and use of process behavior charts is provided in the appendix, along with references for further reading.

# Chapter Four

# Processes and Quality Improvement

As we mentioned in the previous chapter, it is not possible to optimize our system of production by merely optimizing all of the processes. The opposite is true. We may only optimize our system by understanding the contributions made by the individual processes and how they interact within the system of production.

The system of production incorporates the entire value chain: external suppliers, internal suppliers, the resources of production, the process of production, sales and distribution, marketing and consumer research, engineering and design, and customers.* Or alternatively, the system of production may be defined as the combination and interaction of all processes that directly affect the operations of our enterprise.

## Optimization and Systems Integration

The system of production is a closed system. The concept of internal and external value chain components does not apply. All components are internal. There is no differentiation between in-

* Suppliers include all functions that provide resources to the system of production, for example, vendors, buyers and planners, human resources, and inventory control. Processes of production include administrative functions such as finance, customer service, and manufacturing engineering. Engineering and design includes design of processes as well as design of product.

ternal suppliers, for example, and external suppliers (vendors). Customers are part of our system. The interaction of all components must be managed as a system.

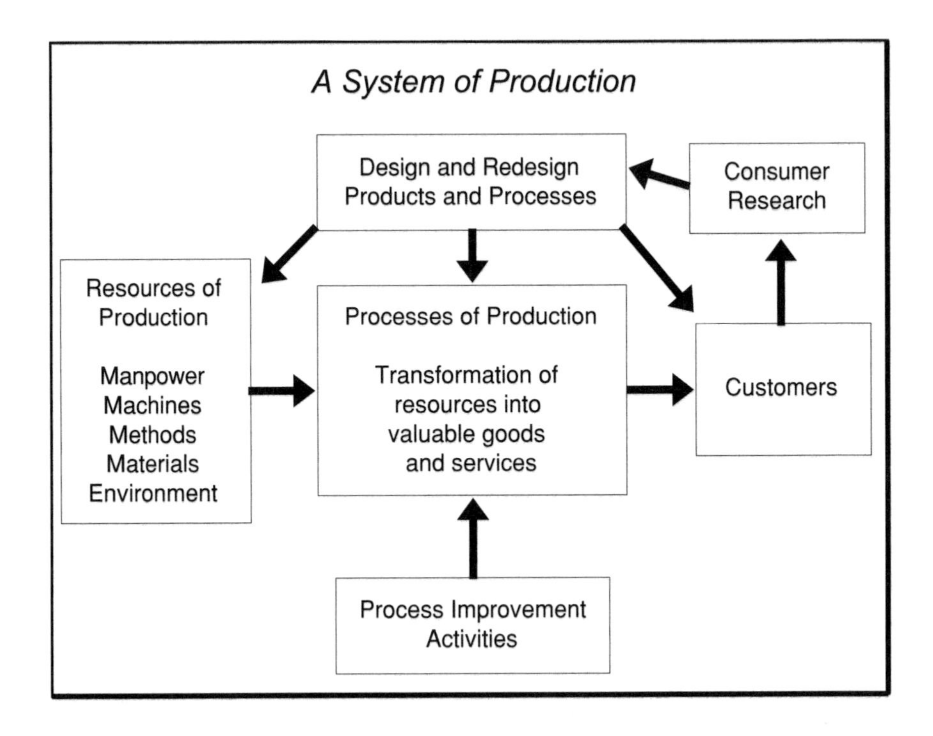


Within this system of production we can define two sub-systems: the technical system and the social system. The technical system consists of processes or methods that are scientific, practical, industrial, and/or mechanical. This system is (or should be) formal and documented. The social system involves human beings working together as a group for common benefit. The social system is informal and undocumented. It is people dealing with people—the way work gets done.

Practical Process Improvement provides methods and tools to reduce variation and improve the technical system. *PPI* also provides people some documented and workable methods and tools to reduce variation in the social system.

An enterprise operates effectively as a system *only* if it has an aim. The aim comes in the form of the statement of purpose (mission) and longer term objectives (vision). When the aim is understood by everyone in the enterprise progress accelerates dramatically. A system of metrics provides the means to measure progress towards achieving the aim.

Efforts in a system are best focused on optimizing the entire system, not on optimizing processes individually. When organizational entities merely optimize their internal processes the result invariably will be a suboptimized system. These entities should focus their efforts on improving the output of the system, not their individual processes. Some components may actually have to be operated in a less than optimal manner in order to optimize the entire system. An example is in order.

Organizations that rely on field service to perform warranty, service, and repair work will often manage the field service function as a profit center. Compensation of individual managers, sales people, and technicians is based on the revenue they generate. Usually, however, costs of material and parts are borne by the operations function. So, it is reasonable to the field service people that any revenue is good revenue. They service everything and anything available—even very old equipment. The cost of providing material and parts for old equipment is often prohibitive. But since the field service people don't see those costs they are oblivious to the problem. Many of their contracts may generate revenue but not profit. When the cost of material and parts is factored in, the enterprise realizes a loss.

A better way would be for enterprise senior managers to organize the field service function so their success reflects not only revenue but costs as well. It may mean less revenue but higher profits.

An even better way would be for field service people to turn their efforts to generating profitable growth, not merely revenue. The effort required for generating work on old equipment would then be turned toward opportunity for growth as well as profit.

*PPI* improvement efforts focus on optimizing the system of production. It is important to recognize the difference between sub-optimizing a component and optimizing the entire system. It is not possible to optimize the system without system-wide cooperation. If people are competing with other people within the system, the enterprise will suffer a loss. A system of competition, after all, derives from winners and losers. In an enterprise, the losses of competition fall directly to bottom line as monetary losses.

Some theorists propose that all competition is bad. This does not seem consistent with the theory of systems management and system optimization. It is absolutely necessary to eliminate competition within the value chain to optimize the enterprise system. However, the notion that the value chain has boundaries suggests that competition likely exists outside of those boundaries. The theorists will counter with, "You have not set your boundaries wide enough." From a practical standpoint, it is not possible to set the boundaries to contain the world, a region, a nation, an economic sector, or even an industry. It is only practical to set our boundaries around our enterprise, incorporating our value chain, including suppliers and customers.

It is true that there are efficiencies and contributions to optimization to be made from cooperating outside of our competitive boundaries. For example, enterprises in an industrial sector may find mutual benefit in establishing standards, sharing production resources, or consolidating the supplier base. But at some point there will be competition. Otherwise, we would not enjoy the benefits that accrue from the capitalist enterprise system.

There are also examples of where our boundaries should be ironclad, shutting out all competitors. Certainly, patents and proprietary designs are a feature of enterprise viability. Proprietary knowledge and the ability to learn and stay ahead of the competition is a significant competitive advantage. So while the spirit of cooperation is alive and well in *PPI*, there are careful delineations where competition is appropriate—outside of the boundaries of our closed enterprise system.

The spirit of cooperation manifests itself in cooperation between and among all components of the value chain. The spirit of cooperation incorporates the continual improvement methodologies. Improvement is the result of a continual, cooperative effort.

Improvement requires change. When any component changes in a closed system there will be a resulting effect on all other components. Closed systems resist change.* This resistance results in *push-back* against the change; it is not only people in the system that cause the resistance. It is also appropriate to think of the resistance as coming from the system itself. The resistance is not always obvious; the push-back may occur in a detached location from the point of pressure. The system tries to adjust to the

* *Le Chatelier's Principle* provides the technical description of a system's resistance to change. "Every change in one of the factors of equilibrium brings about a rearrangement of the system in such a direction as to minimize the original change."

change over time and return to its original condition of equilibrium. That is why *PPI* methodology requires a rigorous control mechanism of team project metrics to track the effectiveness of process improvements.

Additionally, *PPI* reduces the push-back from people by including them in the projects that lead to the change. It is said that people resist change. It is more appropriate to say that people resist change that is forced upon them. If they have a choice, there is no reason to resist. *PPI* puts the people into the process—into the equation—and gives them a part in the outcome. Resistance is reduced greatly. People actually become change agents, not obstructions.

## Value-Added Work and Waste

As we discussed earlier, when customers judge our products and services they are really making decisions of value. That is, they are making a decision about what they are willing to pay for. Clearly they do not want to pay for rework or scrap, unnecessary inspections, or processes that do not contribute directly to the quality of the product. So by extension, customers are also the judge of our work—whether it is value-added work or waste.

Value-added work is a time worn phrase. Sometime in the past it fell out of use because of liberties taken with its definition and application. Value-added could mean anything to anybody. It was even used as a threat, as in, "Your work is not value-added." There was confusion as to who was the judge of value-added. *PPI* eliminates the confusion and resurrects the term as a primary component of the program.

### *Classifications of Work and Waste*

| *Category* | *Classification* |
|---|---|
| Value-added work | Value-added work must satisfy three tests:<br>1. The work done must be something customers are willing to pay for.<br>2. The work done results in an observable and/or measurable change to the thing being worked on.<br>3. The work is done correctly and completely, no inspection is required. |
| Necessary work | Work that does not satisfy the tests for value-added work but is necessary.<br>1. It may not be eliminated.<br>2. Examples include tax preparation, ISO 9000 registration, and government required regulatory work. |
| Unnecessary work | Busy work, red tape, rework, inspections to sort good from bad—work that can be eliminated without affecting customer satisfaction |
| Physical waste | "Stuff" that can be seen or touched, including material or product that is no good, extra or left over material, excessive inventory, scrap and other physical waste |

In order to classify our work, it is necessary to flowchart the process. The *PPI* convention for flowcharting is to imagine you are "the thing" going through the process and identify all of the steps from its perspective.* The flowchart provides a description of the

* This is called a basic flowchart. There are many ways to flowchart a process and we use them all at various times and for various applications in *PPI*. However, we normally begin with a basic flowchart of the thing going through the process.

process as it is currently happening, not how it was designed or how we wish it would be happening. First, we list all of the steps (and stops) the thing makes and what happens to it along the way. Then, we include times for all of the steps and stops, including waiting time.

After our flowchart is completed we can apply the test for value-added work. To be value-added a step in the process must pass three tests:

1. the work done must be something customers are willing to pay for,
2. the work done results in an observable and/or measurable change to the thing being worked on, and
3. the work is done correctly with no need for follow-up inspection.

This is a tough test. If the step fails any of these three criteria, it fails the test.

Usually, only 10% or fewer of the steps in any process pass the test for value-added work, and the value-added steps usually represent less than 2% of the total process time. That is why we can normally achieve a 50% cycle time reduction of any process.

The next category in the hierarchy is necessary work. Much of the non-value-added work may be in this category. However, this is the most dangerous of all categories in which to put work. Why? Because the word "necessary" has connotations inferring the work to be valid when it may not be. In reality, much of what we consider necessary work is not. Let me give you an example.

Credit checks are usually considered in the category of necessary work. But are credit checks really necessary? Why do we do them? We do them because we do not trust our customers. Credit checks result from getting stung in the past. Some companies abuse the process, carrying the practice to ridiculous levels.

Customers are a part of our system of production, just as is a sister plant or another division of our company. Would we require credit checks for another part of our company? No. Nor should we always require credit checks of our customers. Customer relationships should be built on lasting partnerships of mutual trust and accountability. It is true some guard is prudent when you do not have a solid relationship with a customer. But the objective is to embrace all customers as trusted partners in our enterprise system. This takes time, working together for mutual benefit.

Let us discuss further the subject of credit checks. The types and reasons given for credit checks are often amazing. Companies conduct credit checks on:

- Other plants in their own company (There is no logical reason given for this—it just happens).
- The US Government (because they pay slowly and the rules state that any customer not paying in a specified time must be credit-checked for the next purchase).
- Customers who are reciprocal customers; that is, each party buys and sells from each other, and
- All customers, regardless of how long they have been a customer, their payment record, or their relationship to the seller.

Practices such as these, that companies do day in and day out, make them increasingly non-competitive. All of this work is waste. This waste is very costly, not only in terms of time but also in terms of tangible dollars. It reduces customer satisfaction by slowing down processes and by tarnishing the seller's image, thereby reducing sales or sales growth and revenue growth. The culmination is often a seller who can attract no customers except ones that are not credit-worthy. They have annoyed their good customers enough that they have lost them all.

The next category is unnecessary work. This includes busy work, red tape, rework, inspections to sort good product from bad, and any work that can be eliminated without affecting customer satisfaction. This category includes many administrative requirements such as forms and signature approvals.

Signature approvals are a good example of unnecessary work. They result from mistrust, and/or a quest for power. Almost all signature approvals fall in one category or the other. Managers require their signature approval because they do not trust the people working for them, and/or they use signatures to justify and reinforce their power of position. Regarding the first reason, I tell managers, not in jest, that they should never have anyone in their organization they do not trust. The potential losses are too great. If they do not trust their people, they should fire them. Regarding the second reason, managers dwelling on ego have no place in a *PPI* enterprise.

All unnecessary work can be eliminated. It slows us down, adds cost, is distracting, and ultimately affects customer satisfaction very negatively. Customers see the results of unnecessary work as longer lead times, forms, and paperwork. Necessary work takes the form of invoices (yes, invoices are unnecessary if we are true partners with our customers), return material authorizations, and other approvals and administrative requirements.

Elimination of unnecessary work does not happen overnight. Why? We do not build customer and supplier partnerships overnight. It takes hard work and time. But we should never lose sight of the goal to eliminate all unnecessary work and the enormous costs associated with this work.

The final category of waste is physical waste. Physical waste is "stuff" that can be seen or touched, including material or product that is no good, extra or leftover material, excessive inventory, scrap, and other physical waste.

Physical waste is also a dangerous category. It is easy to classify some scrap as necessary. Companies that buy raw material and convert it for use in the production process often view some level of raw material scrap as acceptable. When converting paper into labels, for example, *trim* scrap is often viewed as not only acceptable, but unavoidable as well. This is faulty logic. *All scrap is waste.* In some processes, left over raw material or salvaged scrap may be recycled to the front end of the manufacturing process. Even then, however, there should be efforts to improve the process to eliminate this practice because all, repeat all, scrap is waste.

Waste derives from any work or activity that is not value-added. Waste includes scrap or extra material in any form. Some non-value-added work may be necessary, such as regulatory compliance work. But even though it is necessary, it is still waste. *PPI* methods are designed to reduce waste, starting from the bottom of the hierarchy and moving up. We start with the easy stuff—scrap and other physical waste—and work upward because once the easier waste is out of the way, the more difficult waste becomes easier to reduce.

We are able to define waste, therefore, as the difference between our current level of efficiency and what we could achieve in a perfect system of production. Sources of waste include:

- Unnecessary or restrictive policies and procedures
- Inspections that simply determine good from bad
- Waiting, transporting, unnecessary motion
- Excessive inventory
- Lack of cooperation between departments, divisions, and work groups
- Scrap and defective product
- Competition between or among suppliers
- Rework

The effects of waste include increased cycle time, increased costs, low productivity, demoralized people, and a failing business.

The easiest and preferred way to reduce waste is to focus on the time required for any step or activity in the processes of production to be completed. That is one of the reasons it is so important to accurately flowchart the process under analysis. We prepare our flowchart from the perspective of the thing going through the process and assign times to all steps. Invariably, the steps (including waiting) having large time delays provide the most fruitful areas for waste reduction. If you have a time problem, you have a waste problem. Much of our waste may be eliminated by simply removing steps that do not add value in the eyes of the customer.

As a rule of thumb, each *PPI* project should be able to reduce cycle time by at least 50%. Why is this so? As previously stated, only 10% of our process steps add value, and the time for these steps is usually no more than 2% of the total cycle time. Even considering necessary steps that do not add value, 50% cycle time reduction is an easily achievable goal. It is not uncommon for teams to reduce cycle times much more. I have seen the customer lead time of a circuit board reduced from 110 days to 10 days. I have seen the cycle time of a material-return process reduced from 50 days to less than 5 days. I have seen the customer lead time of an industrial laser reduced from 16 weeks to less than 4. I have seen the customer lead time of industrial, high-capacity filters reduced from 2 weeks to 1 day. 50% is always an achievable goal.

Practical Process Improvement makes everyone in the enterprise CEO of their own job. In order to achieve the kind of cycle time reductions cited above, it is necessary to put this idea into practice. In order to do so, it is appropriate to consider responsibility and accountability. We are usually pretty proficient at assigning responsibility, but as our processes grow up around these assignments they make accountability almost impossible to assign. Why? Because the traditional methods of management assume that people are the source of problems. We *blame* people. Assigning blame is one of the most damaging and costly practices in industry today. People are not the source of problems; people hold the key to the solutions to problems. Assigning blame is irresponsible and costly because people will hide problems to keep from being blamed in the future.

We do, however, need to assign clear responsibility and accountability. If an individual is incapable of accepting these assignments it will be necessary to make an adjustment. Sometimes, merely a reassignment of work is all that is required. At other times, however, other action will be indicated. If we are not able to trust an individual we must act decisively and quickly. Since *PPI* assigns control of work to the people, we must ensure that we have the right people. There is nothing more demoralizing to an organization than to be encumbered with problem people.

In any population, it will be possible to identify some people who exhibit personality characteristics or other traits that make it difficult, if not impossible, for them to be assimilated fully into a *PPI* enterprise. These people will not only be miserable, they will transmit misery to everyone they come in contact with. It is the enlightened manager's duty to find another place for these people where they have a chance of finding joy in their work.

## Processes and Variation

To review: a system of production consists of the interaction between resources and processes, resulting in products. There are five resources of production—we call them the "4 Ms and an E"—manpower, machines, material, methods, and the environment. Process behavior charts operationally define our processes. These charts are designed to identify and quantify the amount and type of process variation.

There are two sources of variation—*special* causes and *common* causes. *Special cause* variation is assignable to a specific resource or cause or event, and it characterizes an unstable, unpredictable process. *Common cause* variation results from the interaction of the resources of production, and it characterizes a stable, predictable process.

Even if a process is stable and predictable, it may not produce high quality output. The process may not be operating on target or the natural variation may exceed the specifications. If a process is unpredictable, even if it is currently providing conforming product, there is no way to know what the process will yield in the future—next year, next month, next week, or even tomorrow.

We can eliminate or reduce variation by analyzing the process using a process behavior chart. Within the *PPI* framework, the steps in this analysis are as follows.

1. Determine if the problem under examination is caused by *common* causes of variation or *a special* cause. It will *always* be necessary to use process behavior charts to make this determination. The problem comes when we try to rely on *common sense* and the *eyeball* method of determining the source of problems. Discovery of the causes of problems resulting from variation is only possible using a process behavior chart. There is no shortcut.

2. If the variation results from a *special* cause, fix it. If the fix is easy, move quickly. If the fix is not so easy, or if it is costly, prudence is in order and potential fixes should be thoroughly tested before implementation.

3. If the problem results from common causes of variation, it will be impossible to identify a single root cause. In this case, we employ a *PPI* project team, made up of employees selected for their competence and knowledge of the process under examination, because the only solution will be to change the process in some fundamental way.

A common tactic used in process analysis is to compare the "voice of the customer" with the "voice of the process." The voice of the customer is the desired state, often characterized by specifications, consumer research, design requirements, and customer desires—stated and unstated. The voice of the process is what the process is currently producing. The voice of the process determines the actual quality. The process quality is determined by the interaction of resources within the process. The voice of the process is operationally defined by a process behavior chart.

In order to achieve quality in the eyes of the customer—customer satisfaction—it is necessary to match the two voices. It is tempting at times to try to adjust the voice of the customer. We often hear statements like, "Our customers really don't know what they want." These types of statements are very dangerous. They would be better stated as, "We are not smart enough to figure out what our customers want." *PPI* is not about redefining customer requirements; it is about meeting customer requirements.

Many programs use the catch phrase, "exceed customer requirements." Is this possible? Probably not and here is why. You will recall our discussion of conditioning and anticipation. You may exceed a customer's requirement or desire one time, but then the product quality is incorporated into the expectations for the next time. So to try to exceed expectations may sound like a noble goal, but it is more likely a buzzword for a hollow program.

Our goal is to match the voice of the process with the voice of the customer. Progressive enterprises strive constantly and forever in this endeavor. This requires teamwork, continual improvement, and use of the appropriate analysis.

## The *PDSA* Model and Continual Improvement

The *PDSA* model was developed from the method scientists use routinely to conduct experiments, to validate hypotheses, make a scientific determination, or to move forward a body of knowledge. *PDSA* is established as the basic improvement model for *PPI*. There are four components: Plan, Do, Study, Act.

- **Plan**: We plan our improvement effort to ensure we are focused on the problem and the desired results. This phase includes defining the project, defining the process, and identifying the source of variation we are dealing with—

*special* causes or *common* causes.

- **Do**: Take appropriate action. If we are dealing with a *special* cause, we take action on that *special* cause. If we are dealing with *common* causes, we analyze the process to determine the source of the problem and make corrective actions. Our motto for this phase is, "In God we trust, all others must bring data." Data is used appropriately for analysis, not merely numerical and statistical gyrations. The output of our analysis is a proposed solution or solutions, ready to be tested.

- **Study**:* Before full scale implementation of our solution(s) it will be necessary to test the solutions on a small scale and study the outcome to ensure that results are appropriate. If we are fortunate and have done our analysis well, the outcome of our test will support the solution(s). We must, however, be willing to accept that our solutions may be incomplete or even incorrect. If our solutions never fail, we should question our testing techniques. If we never take the time to test and study the solutions before implementation, we will be taking a great risk.

- **Act**: Based on our analysis, solutions, implementation, and test results it will be necessary to take action. If the test outcome is good, we will be able to move forward with fuller scale implementation. If the test outcome falls short it will be necessary to return to the Planning step and conduct the cycle again.

---

* In some applications of this model, *study* is changed to *check*. The word check has a totally different connotation from the word study. Check is cursory. Study implies a thorough test of a hypothesis. So, in the *PPI* program, we use the word study. We test our proposed solutions thoroughly, study the results of the test, and act on those results appropriately.

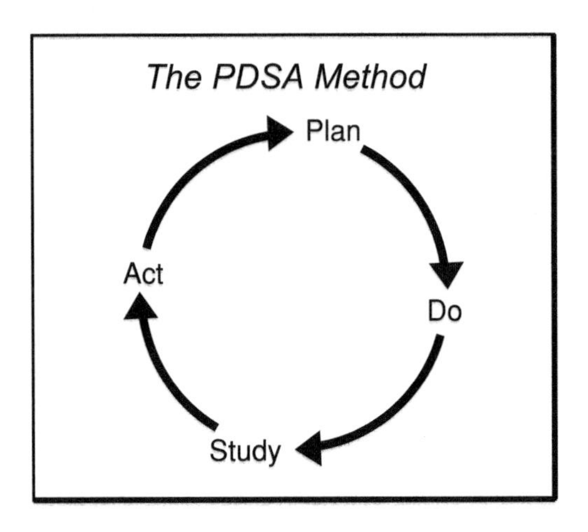


## Learning and Change

The objective of Practical Process Improvement is profit. Profit comes from reducing waste and costs as well as increasing revenue through customer satisfaction and growth. *PPI* achieves results by improving the processes of production in ways that optimize the entire system of production, not merely the components in isolation.

Results are often confused with better numbers. There are many ways to get better numbers. The easiest way is to simply change them. I once knew a plant comptroller who did this regularly to give upper management the numbers they wanted. It happens more often than we would care to admit.

Another way to get better numbers is to change the formula—the way the numbers are computed. Denominator management is an example. We can get much better numbers by changing the way we measure or compute the denominator in a ratio. The earlier example regarding *DPMO* computation for circuit board quality level is an object lesson of this practice.

There are certainly other ways to get better numbers without changing anything substantially. These will only be limited by the ingenuity of *creative* people. But, they are false improvements. The only true improvement comes from improvements in the processes of production, and these must support efforts to optimize the entire enterprise, or they too will be false improvements.

Improving our processes and optimizing our system of production requires learning new and better ways to do things—to change from the old way of doing things to the new. Changes bring about individual and organizational dynamics which may not be ignored if sustainable improvement is the goal.

It is imperative to begin with the underlying belief in the value of people. It is not appropriate to blame people. Blaming people will only make things worse. Processes, with all their flaws, got that way over time. It is no one's fault. Less than 1% of the problems in any process are due to people in the process. The problems in the process are primarily due to the interaction of the resources within the process. Most people are doing their best.

It will be impossible to improve our processes unless we change something. But change, merely for the sake of change, is not the goal. We must create a learning environment where it is everyone's job to understand the *PPI* methods for continual improvement and change.

It is a false hope, as well, to assume that processes left alone will continue to run smoothly. The old saying, "If it ain't broke, don't fix it" should be changed to, "If it ain't broke, it soon will be." If we do not constantly and forever take action to improve our process they will not stay the same. They will deteriorate through entropy. Entropy is universal, acting on all systems and processes. Entropy is relentless, and the disarray of the system will increase accordingly when left alone.

We often hear the statement that people resist change. More accurately, people resist *being* changed. People resist change when it is forced upon them. When people have a choice, however, there is no reason to resist. *PPI*, therefore, involves people in the analytical process so that they are part of the change determination. Unfortunately, it is not always possible to involve everyone on the team responsible for the change. It is, therefore, important that managers understand the dynamics of change and how those dynamics operate in the workplace.

When people are forced to undergo change they undergo a predictable cycle of emotional steps or phases.

## The Phases of Change

1. Shock or Denial:
   The first reaction to a significant change is normally expressed as disbelief, ignoring the change, or unwillingness to accept that a change is occurring.

2. Emotional Outlet, usually Anger:
   Once people work through the first stage, they usually exhibit a flood of emotions, almost always anger. This anger is often mistaken for obstinacy, but it is merely part of the process of working through the change.

3. Bargaining:
   This phase or stage is characterized by delaying tactics and attempts to deflect the change. People in this phase are actually bargaining from a position of anxiety—What do I get? What do I lose? and, Will I keep my job? Even if the change is positive people will be asking the same question, "Where will I end up?"

4. Depression:
   This is not depression in the clinical sense, but rather, it is grief. People are grieving because all change produces loss and all loss must be grieved.

5. Acceptance:
   The final phase or stage is acceptance. But it comes in two forms. First is merely intellectual acceptance. People have accepted the change intellectually, but their underlying fears and anxiety have not been resolved. The second type is emotional acceptance. This is the goal. When people reach emotional acceptance, the change process is complete.

## Managing Change

It is important to remember that this process is not only normal, it is necessary. It is the personification of the emotional healing process brought about by any significant change or loss. It is also important to note that this process takes, at a minimum, 18 months to complete. While it might be possible to achieve intellectual acceptance more quickly, emotional acceptance takes time.

When we view the change process in this way. it explains why we see a great deal of anger, bargaining, and depression. We perceive this because people are reacting to significant changes in their lives. This change process is an emotional process, not a behavioral process, and this is an important distinction. People are constantly going through these phases or stages—the rapidity and constancy of change in today's society will see to that. But these are feelings, not behaviors. It is okay for people to feel angry, but it is not okay for them to act out that anger inappropriately.

The key to helping people and the organization through the change process is communication. If we withhold information from people, we only raise their level of anxiety and make things worse. Yet, the common practice is to keep changes *secret* until a formal announcement. Rumors start flying.

In the past, we have tended to believe that we should protect ourselves and/or our people from undo stress leading up to a change. But when we withhold information from people, they make up their own version of what is happening. People are not stupid; they know when a change is in the works. And their own version is usually a far worse fantasy than the actual change.

So within the *PPI* paradigm, the information flow opens up. *We understand that people handle bad news better than no news.* We keep people informed at all steps along the way. If people mishandle the information, then other action should be taken. But to withhold information because of one or two gossip mongers only plays on the fears and anxiety that is building up across the organization. The best way to reduce the anxiety level that accompanies any significant change is to increase communication.

Finally, if not carefully managed, the dynamics of the change process creates a risk—a risk that people will begin thinking of themselves as victims—then we have a real problem on our hands. When people think they are victims, they begin to act like victims. When they act like victims, their energy level and problem-solving abilities deteriorate significantly.

We must help people stay out of the victim role. How do we do this? We keep them involved—informed. We help them become problem solvers. Then their energy level and participation level increases. By involving everyone in the *PPI* program, we will be able increase the energy level of the entire enterprise. Together we become the pathfinders in the journey toward continual improvement, customer satisfaction, and profitable growth.

## Summary

In this chapter we have discussed the *PPI* process for improving productivity and quality. It is a proven method, including simple statistical practices that are more than mere placebos. The process behavior chart is the foundation of the Practical Process Improvement method. When used within the *PPI* program, it provides the most powerful tool available for improving enterprise profitability.

In the past, managers have relegated application of process behavior charts only to manufacturing processes. Within the *PPI* program, process behavior charts are used in *all* process of production.

# Chapter Five

## Guidelines for Success

In the preceding three chapters we discussed customer satisfaction, production methods, and the concepts and theory behind process improvement. Now we will review some basic principles of *PPI* management:

- Any enterprise needs to be managed as a system. This system includes suppliers, customers, and internal components.
- The enterprise system needs an aim. This takes the form of a statement of purpose (the mission), a longer term objective (the vision), and a system of metrics so we may know what we have achieved. Executive management is responsible for creating these components.
- It is necessary to create a learning environment. This not only allows people the freedom to learn and improve, it also provides a powerful competitive advantage.
- All of our improvement efforts should aim to optimize the system, not merely the components. In order to do this, we will have to establish relationships within the value chain based on mutual trust and accountability. Distrust is inefficient and expensive.
- The enterprise is in business to provide valuable goods and services to customers. Therefore, customers must be the focus of everything we do.

- Quality is not merely conformance to specifications. Quality is a matter of customer judgment. Quality results from the interaction of forces within our processes of production. There are some simple and powerful statistical methods and tools to operationally define our processes.

Those discussions provide a backdrop for this chapter that will deal with some specific guidelines for success. Together, these guidelines provide a strategy for leading the enterprise to market leadership.

## Guidelines for Success

1. *Solutions should support the company's strategies for improving profitability. We must never lose sight of the aim: to improve profits in order to stay in business and provide long term stability and employment security.*

The goal of Practical Process Improvement is to increase profit. The equation for profit is:

$$\text{Profit} = \text{Revenue} - \text{Cost}$$

Cost is reduced through application of the "prevention" method of quality assurance, waste removal, and process improvement. There are three ways to increase revenue:

1. When we improve quality, we increase customer satisfaction and enjoy increasing sales in turn.
2. Because with *PPI* we are continually reducing our cost of production, it is possible to reduce our price to increase revenue through volume.
3. We may be able to combine and/or manage some combination of 1 and 2. This is optimum.

We decrease waste and the costs of scrap and rework when we improve quality of products and services, using *PPI*. Our productivity improves. As we improve customer satisfaction we are able to capture the market with quality and/or price. The enterprise is successful. Everyone contributes to this success, for a successful enterprise provides employment security.

2. *Solutions should improve the desired company-level metric(s) from which the team project was derived.*

The system of metrics focuses on customer satisfaction and the prevention of problems by using appropriate measurements and methods. In addition, the Steering Committee utilizes the system of metrics to determine important shortfalls and gaps for assignment to *PPI* teams.

The system of metrics supports the aim of the enterprise. Statistical methods—process behavior charts—are employed so that leaders may understand the basis of shortfalls and the type of variation they are dealing with. Appropriate identification of the magnitude and type of variation is the first step to process analysis and preventive action. When we have a predictable process, metrics can be a guide to the future. Predictable processes are operationally defined by process behavior charts.

The system of metrics provides indicators of progress. When progress falls short, the system of metrics provides an indication of where to concentrate scarce resources and leadership attention on important problems. It can take the guesswork out of what to assign teams to improve.

3. *Solutions should focus on improving product and services with the aim of customer satisfaction.*

Within the *PPI* management system, the focus of all our efforts is on the customer. Care must be taken to ensure efforts are concentrated to that end. The objective is to continually remove non-value-added work from our system of production. It is a mistake to waste valuable time and attention on work and processes that do not add value to the product or service in the eyes of the customer. It is a mistake to make more efficient a process that is not needed in the first place.

Customer satisfaction is not a vague concept: there are ways to measure its elements. If we are to know how we are doing, these elements must be incorporated into our system of metrics. The Five Elements of Customer Satisfaction are:

1. Quality of product or service
2. Availability (on-time delivery)
3. Price
4. Image
5. Anticipation

4. *We should not* rely *on "screening inspection" (sorting good from bad) to achieve quality. Quality and productivity are achieved simultaneously only when nonconforming items are no longer produced. Inspections of some sort will always be necessary. For example, when the risk of loss is great we should inspect for compliance or safety on a regular basis (example: a pre-flight inspection). Never institute inspection on people (policeman role). People are not the problem; results come from the interaction of forces within the processes of production.*

It is easy to misunderstand this guideline. It is, therefore, appropriate to expand upon it. First, screening inspection/sorting is detection-based quality assurance. Any good-bad determination is an inspection based on detection methodology. It need not be the subject of a formal inspection. Any computation of yield is based on a count of good and bad. The objective is to move away from these methods toward meaningful measurement, analysis, and prevention. Of course the only way to do this is to learn how to operate our processes so that they produce 100% conforming product predictably—which will eliminate the need for screening. We learn how to do this by understanding and using process behavior charts. Learning to use processbehavior charts will not happen overnight. It will be an achievement, arising over time out of hard work and diligent application.

There is nothing wrong with 100% screening inspection that money won't cure—it is terrifically expensive. In today's market, 100% screening is not sustainable, because while it may be effective, it is just too costly—and never as effective as we would hope.

Systems and methods that rely on inspecting and prodding people are based on distrust. These methods are inefficient and expensive, because they never allow people to work to their full potential. Most signature approvals fall within the category of the policeman role. Signature approvals may be necessary but only for the most sensitive and risky issues.

There are situations when 100% inspection is necessary. It is important to distinguish appropriate inspections from screening inspections. The former are part of any good operating procedure, while screening is merely a sorting process. Examples of appropriate inspections would include:

- Dangerous working conditions with people at risk must be constantly inspected for hazards.
- High-risk situations such as a nuclear power plants.

There are also some circumstances when screening is necessary—we have no choice.

- When we are producing very costly products or when cost of repair is very high.
- New products that have not been thoroughly tested or evaluated should be screened until the bugs have been worked out.

100% screening may be necessary at certain times and situations, but the cost of doing business this way should never be overlooked. In most industrial processes appropriate use of process behavior charts will allow us to move away from 100% screening. When we learn how to operate our processes predictably and capably we can eliminate screening inspection entirely.

5. *We should move to supplier relationships based on trust and mutual accountability. These relationships are established over time through dedicated effort of all parties. Only when we have established these relationships and suppliers become capable and predictable, will it be possible to reap the benefits of sole sourcing, just-in-time operations, and lean production.*

Suppliers are part of our system, part of the value chain, not external entities. We should move toward win-win relationships based on mutual trust and accountability. Win-win is not merely "I win, you win." In this context, win-win is, "I can only win if you win. You can only win if I win. If either fails, we both fail."

Through achieving this interdependence, we move to preventive actions and away from simply reacting.

Creating interdependence is hard work. It is an achievement accomplished over time. Interdependent relationships once established, however, are rugged and durable. They are also very efficient because all parties are working toward the same goals.

Suppliers include all people, entities, and organizations that supply resources to the system of production. Resources include: manpower, machines, material, methods, and environment. So suppliers include human resources, finance, industrial and manufacturing engineering, and others not traditionally thought of as suppliers.

6. *Never look at costs based on isolated data. The cost of anything—a part, a service, a step in a process—should only be evaluated in light of total costs. Optimizing total savings may require us to increase the price we pay for some elements in the short term.*

This strategy has been around a long time. You will find few these days who would express contrary logic. Yet, the actualization of this strategy is seldom achieved

It is easy to visualize this strategy in the idea of incoming material. If we save a $1.00 for a part from a cheaper vendor, but add 30 minutes of assembly time because of poor fit, it is easy to see the false economy. There are, additionally, more subtle applications:

- Pursue an annoying credit check routine for all customers. This may drive off good customers, leaving behind the credit risks.
- Establish rewards for managers requiring that they reduce their own unit cost, or increase their own unit profit, re-

gardless of the consequences elsewhere.

- Reduce inventory to save money: run out of parts, delay production, ship late, and lose customers.
- Rely on an end-of-quarter push to *deliver* the sales quota. This conditions your customers to order late in order to get a deal. This can result in less revenue, costly stockpiles to meet *the crunch*, heroic efforts, and tons of overtime.

7. *Recognize that people resist being changed. All change brings about anxiety—fear of the unknown. Anxiety is reduced when people know what is happening or about to happen. Therefore, in order to reduce anxiety we must increase communications flow and involve all stakeholders in the change process. Solutions should improve stakeholders' pride of involvement and workmanship.*

Even if the change is positive, everyone affected will be asking the same question, "Where am I going to end up?" This question is accompanied by fear and anxiety that results from people not knowing what's in store and how they will come out of the change.

The way to resolve anxiety is through communication. People need to be told what is in store for them. They need to be told how they will come out of the change. People need to be told what is going on, even if the news is bad. People handle bad news better than no news.

Managers need to manage the change process in ways that help employees stay out of the victim role. How? Managers need to stay out of the blame game—blaming automatically results in victims. People doing their best know that emerging problems are usually not their fault. Problems result from the process itself.

*8. Standardize all new processes within the ISO 9000 framework.*

A primary theme of this book is process improvement through waste removal. An equally important theme is reduction of variation that occurs in the process, in the resources of the process, and in the way people operate the process. It is not enough to take out waste. Taking out waste improves our cycle times and efficiency. But to truly improve quality it is necessary to reduce variation.

ISO 9000 is a tool that can be used very effectively to manage and reduce variation. How? When we document a procedure we create a standard for consistently operating the process. We create a standard for training. And, we create a standard for understanding how the process operates thereby making improvement easier.

Within the *PPI* program, ISO 9000 is a valuable tool to standardize improvements and standardize the way people operate their processes. Recent iterations of the standard require continual improvement as well, and *PPI* provides a method for compliance. The world market place views ISO 9000 as a minimum requirement. In addition to being a valuable quality tool, it may be a valuable tool for marketing, merchandising, and sales. Adding ISO certification to an enterprise's credentials will certainly add positively to its image.

9. *Provide standardized training, now and in the future. Worker training worker is the path to chaos.*

In Strategy 8 we discussed utilizing ISO 9000 as a tool to reduce variation. Another even more valuable tool to reduce variation and improve quality is training. Unfortunately, many companies view training as an unnecessary expense and avoid formal training programs. Training is often the first item cut in the budget review process. The managers in these companies truly believe they are reducing costs. Little do they know how costly the lack of standardized training really is. The losses from poor training far exceed the cost of good training.

Contrast this with the general manager for the Toyota UK assembly plant who commented that at start up he had 1400 employees and was making *no cars*. His job was to keep everyone in the proper training and cross-training programs.*

The greatest cost of the lack of training is the increased variation introduced into the processes of production from workers trying to do their best—but all doing it differently. It is illustrative to think of the childhood game "Telephone." In this game the teacher starts the process by whispering something in the ear of the closest child. Then, in turn, each child passes on the phrase to the next child. Giggles ensue and laughter erupts at the end when the phrase is totally nonsensical and entirely different from the original phrase. This is only a game, but the same principle applies in worker training worker—a very expensive way of doing business.

We assume that each worker is following the standard proce-

* My thanks to Dr. Donald J. Wheeler for this anecdote.

dure when, in reality, they are putting their spin on the process. These deviations are never good, because they introduce unwanted variation and unpredictability into the processes of production. When these habits are passed on through worker-training-worker programs, it is just like the telephone game. The result is a process that is operating differently from the standard process, often to the point of being nonsensical.

Training is not an expense. Training is an investment in our most valuable resource—people. Training must be standardized with qualified trainers and standardized programs. We need not hire extra people as trainers; rather, certify existing workers and provide them the time and resources necessary to conduct standardized training. This should not involve large expenditures.

10. *Ensure that all solutions are tested and achieve the desired results; never leave it to chance or speculation. This means, among other things, that we must be willing to accept that our solutions may be incomplete or incorrect. Using the PDSA method will lead to certainty.*

Testing solutions, using the *PDSA* method, is built into Practical Process Improvement within Step Six of The Eight Step Method. This principle applies to all improvmenent activities for it is only possible to know if our solutions are valid by applying the *PDSA* mehtod. Additionally, managers should test all their decisions and directives before implementation. It is safe to say that managers seldom do this. But it is important to recognize that decisions or directives may not produce the expected results. To ignore this guideline will result in the worst kind of expense—expense from the unknown, including unrecognized losses and opportunity costs.

The job of management is predicting and making decisions to prevent unwanted situations from developing. Inherent in the manager's job is the requirement of self evaluation—following up to ensure that decisions actually produce desired results. Unfortunately, managers seldom if ever do this. But we are lucky, because process behavior charts provide the answer. These tools, once established, require little or no time to maintain and they will accurately measure actual accomplishment and validate our decisions.

## Summary

These guidelines transcend the *PPI* program to successful management in general. Together, they provide a strategy for leading the enterprise to market leadership. The take-away is that without employing these strategies, *PPI* success will be only relative. Further, these strategies serve well for the success of any enterprise, regardless of programs and/or tactics employed. They are appropriate in solving problems; they are instructive when leading the enterprise in preventive actions.

# Chapter Six

# Management Involvement

It is appropriate to think of three levels of management involvement: buy-in, participation, and involvement. Let's look at all three.

We used to talk about management buy-in. We used phrases like, "In order to be successful, this program will need management buy-in." But then we realized that this approach was not enough, so we evolved to management participation. Now we used phrases like, "In order to be successful, managers must participate in this program." But the catch was that managers could satisfy either of these requirements by delegation. Managers could participate by identifying *experts* to delegate their involvement to. Slice it any way you want, this was still delegation, not involvement.

Within Practical Process Improvement, the acceptable role for management is *involvement*. There are certain, specific roles and responsibilities that managers may not delegate. (These roles will be examined in detail in Part Two.) *PPI* does not require all of our time, but it does require involvement with duties that may not be delegated.

If managers choose not to be involved in *PPI* the organization will be wasting its time and resources. (This extends to any worthwhile endeavor. If management is not involved in meaningful ways, enterprise level programs will not be successful.) While

*PPI* may pay some near-term benefits, full potential will only be realized through meaningful management involvement.

There are four types of managers that will be encountered during *PPI* implementation, as displayed in the following matrix.

| **Type 1** | **Type 2** |
|---|---|
| Achieve their objectives and goals<br>Involved in the PPI Program | Achieve their objectives and goals<br>Not involved in the PPI Program |
| **Type 3** | **Type 4** |
| Fall short on their objectives and goals<br>Involved in the PPI Program | Fall short on their objectives and goals<br>Not involved in the PPI Program |

Type 1 and type 4 managers are easy to deal with. Type 1 managers are our achievers—those who are destined for greater responsibilities. Type 4 managers are not fitting in and are probably not happy in their jobs. They should be helped to find a job elsewhere, where they will be happy. Type 2 and type 3, however, are tough to deal with. Type 2 managers are achieving their objectives and goals, but they are not supporting the *PPI* program. These managers will put us to the test. Type 3 managers, while supporting the *PPI* program, are still not achieving their objectives and goals. These managers also present a challenge.

Using traditional thinking we would have kept the Type 2 managers. After all, they are making their numbers. Likewise, Type 3 managers would have been "counseled" to improve and would have been considered lower rung managers, probably not long for the organization. But within the *PPI* management method, we look at these two types of managers in a different way.

Type 2 managers are sending a clear signal, "I will only participate if I feel like it." It is important to recognize that this attitude will undermine not only the *PPI* program but any other program they don't feel like supporting. They will eventually create bigger problems—it is good to identify them early. They have to go.

Type 3 managers, on the other hand, are sending a signal that is just as clear: they are loyal and they are doing their best. We keep type 3 managers. They will be given training and coaching; maybe simply rearranging work is all that is necessary. If, in the longer run, type 3 managers are not able to keep up, then some other adjustments will be made. Experience shows, however, that they will not only do fine, they will form the backbone of continual improvement efforts and be instrumental in enterprise success.

Type 1, Type 3, and Type 4 managers are easy to identify. Type 2 managers are not. There is, however, a telltale sign. Type 2 managers are easily identified when they present you with the following: "Okay, I will do *PPI* but I only have so many hours in the day. What do you want me to give up?" Good leaders do not let type 2 managers get away with this strategy.

## The Manager's Role

Some believe that the primary role of a manager is to deal effectively with daily challenges, remove obstacles, and resolve predicaments. They take action to correct problems based on experience and *gut feel*. This way of managing is prevalent in many enterprises, but it is simply reacting. While there are times reaction is our only option, reaction does not lead to improvement, only correction. Gut feel is little more than guessing.

Reacting does not improve things, but identifying the causes of variation and removing their effects will. Within the *PPI* model, the manager's role changes from reacting to problems to proactive involvement. We call this leadership. Leadership within the *PPI* model is not just a motivational issue; leadership is looking to the future, understanding the source of problems, substituting analysis for gut feel, and taking action to prevent problems from recurring. The *PPI* model focuses on the customer, with a goal of achieving market leadership.

The *PPI* model of leadership requires a transformation from traditional management and gut feel reactions to proactive management and action based on analysis and data.

## Historical Perspective

The Practical Process Improvement model recognizes that the management systems currently in place have evolved into their present state. Some quality and productivity improvement models propose eliminating many current practices. Some propose wholesale replacement. It might be nice to wholly transform current practices, but it is not practical. The *PPI* model provides the guidelines, concepts, methods, and tools to effectively employ modern management systems in a proactive way. It is important that managers understand the derivation and limitations of current practices in order to better understand what must be done to make *PPI* effective.

The biggest challenge to most managers is the lack of time to deal with all of the challenges that arise. Because of a lack of time it is not possible for one manager to do everything. Managerial systems have evolved primarily to solve this problem. Managers delegate work to subordinate managers. This concept is called *span of control.* Each manager, at each layer, has a span of control over a number of people and amount of work that they are able to accomplish efficiently. Let's take a look at how these systems evolved.

In pre-industrial, times span of control was a non-problem. In the days of the artisan, the manager (the artisan) was a complete system of production, including one on one customer interface. But that changed in the late Eighteenth Century with the introduction of interchangeable parts. With interchangeable parts came industrial production. The manager's job changed from making and selling product to supervision of others making and selling product. Span of control became the issue.

The discipline of Scientific Management, introduced early in the Twentieth Century, attempted to address the problem of span of control (as well as quality control and productivity improvement). Within this discipline, the buzz word was "scientific" placement of workers within the system of production, under managers assigned by function. In reality, this method was little more than mechanically placing the workers in an assembly line.

Nevertheless, it became necessary to deploy layers of management and supervision according to the span of control limitations, resulting in the layered organization chart with which we are all familiar. This method of management provided two important functions. First, it provided a way to prod workers efficiently. Just as important, it provided a convenient way to place blame.*

About the middle of the Twentieth Century, organizational experts began to deal with the problems inherent in management layering. A discipline emerged, commonly referred to as Management by Objective (or MBO). A better name would have been Management by Results, for now the job of the manager shifted from managing people to simply managing the results—the output of the system of production. The battle cry now became, "I don't care how you get the results, just get them." Human resource structures (management schemes) evolved around this concept, including annual objectives, merit pay, annual reviews, and matrix organizations. Leadership was replaced by bureaucracy.

Then, in the last two decades of the Twentieth Century, along came the *Quality Revolution* and we were taught that MBO, annual objectives, merit pay, and annual reviews were evil things. But most managers did not agree with this assignment. Why? Because as the management function evolved, moving backwards to a span of less control has never been an option. Managers have limited personal time and attention. Good managers juggle many tasks and do them well. They are able to choose correctly

* Another name for this style of management is "train wreck management." During this era, the number of railroad lines in the country was growing rapidly, accompanied by many train wrecks. It was important to put in place a management structure that allowed efficient assignment of blame for the wrecks.

what they devote their time to and what they delegate. Managers have become reliant on these management schemes—there is no other way to get the job done within the current paradigm.

While we may debate the evil of the aforementioned management schemes, one principle of leadership has not changed: The personal attention of the leader is required to ensure that the important things get done. Good leaders pay personal attention to those things that, in their judgment, will be most successful for the enterprise, and most successful for their careers. They delegate the remaining priorities to subordinate managers. The challenge is making correct decisions about what to delegate; to move from bureaucracy to leadership.

## Reactive Managers and Leaders

So there are two fundamental methods of management. The first emphasizes waiting for problems and reacting to them as they arise. The second emphasizes leadership: analysis, correcting the source of problems, and a focus on the customer. We can generally categorize managers as reactive or leaders by their use of one approach or the other.

1. Reactive Manager: "Wonder what problems people are going to send my way today?"
2. Leader: "What will I do today to get ahead of the needs of my customers and the challenges of the competition? Will I be proactive or reactive? Will I merely react all day to problems as they arise or will I spend my time preventing problems from happening in the future?"

Practical Process Improvement emphasizes leadership and a proactive approach. But we still have the problem of time: *How do*

*I as a manager find time to solve the problems that are facing me today and find the time to use PPI methods and tools in a more proactive approach*? We are reminded of the saying, "When we are up to our hips in alligators, it is difficult to remember that we came to drain the swamp."

We are lucky. It is not necessary to choose one path at the expense of the other. Practical Process Improvement provides concepts, methods, and tools to do both—to take a proactive approach *without* sacrificing our ability to deal with the problems facing us on a daily basis. *PPI* methods and tools provide a clear choice regarding what should be delegated and what should not.

As the *PPI* program matures, managers are able to spend more of their time looking to the future and less time on solving problems—more time being proactive, less time reacting to problems. They are able to focus on customers and the market place with the goal of market leadership. They are able to determine easily those issues that they need to address personally and those that may be delegated.

How does *PPI* do this? The Practical Process Improvement model incorporates the prevention method of production and quality assurance. The tools associated with this method are very powerful. The goal is to be continually increasing revenue and reducing costs. The *PPI* method removes the sources of problems to prevent them from recurring. This frees up time to concentrate on the customer and market leadership.

Remember, *PPI* is not business as usual. It is not just common sense—for what is common sense to you may not be common sense to me. Practical Process Improvement is built upon the foundation of logic, the appropriate use of data, the power of people, and the desire to succeed. The management methods are prescriptive, not voluntary. This is not a pick-and-choose program. The Practical Process Improvement model is a *system* for enterprise management, continual improvement, profit, and market leadership.

To review: the primary elements of the Practical Process Improvement Management Method include:

1. managing and optimizing our enterprise as a system, not merely pasting together groups or units;
2. understanding variation and its affect on quality, using appropriate statistical tools (primarily the process behavior chart) to reduce variation and its effects, and improving the processes of production;
3. understanding that people are a resource, not the source of problems, understanding how to manage them and the change process accordingly; and
4. accomplishing this within an organizational climate attuned to learning and innovation, focused on the customer.

## Summary

Let's summarize this chapter with one final point on management involvement. It is vital that all of our activities, strategies, and systems are built on trust and mutual accountability. We cannot afford to employ people whom we distrust. It will be impossible for us to get where we want to go unless we are able to trust everyone in our system of production.

The surest way to create untrustworthy people is to not trust them and then treat them like they are not trusted. The surest way to create trustworthy people is to trust them. People who are trusted will normally fulfill their responsibilities and exceed our expectations.

Trust is paramount within the *PPI* model. But action must be swift and decisive when someone proves that they are not trustworthy. There is no room for untrustworthy people in today's enterprise. Distrust is a very expensive proposition.

# Part Two

# The *PPI* Process

# Chapter Seven

# The *PPI* Organization & Support System

Many quality improvement models have been presented as a "journey," not a program. The rationale: The quest for quality is never ending. While this is true, it is very difficult to manage a never-ending journey. It is much easier to manage a program. Modern managers receive extensive training in program management, very little in journey management. They have experience managing programs, not journeys.

Therefore, the Practical Process Improvement system was developed as a program with specific duties, responsibilities, and a well defined organization and support system.

## Steering Committee

The primary component of the *PPI* organization and support system is the Steering Committee. The composition of the Steering Committee is the CEO, senior executives/staff, and principal *PPI* coordinating managers. Their purpose is to execute the enterprise business strategy, guide enterprise activities, and provide leadership. Leadership includes making the *PPI* program successful.

In large enterprises there may be more than one level or layer of executive management. Steering Committees are then formed at each level with supporting policies, guidance, strategic plans and aims, and metrics. Each subordinate Steering Committee provides ever increasing details for business strategy execution and *PPI* integration.

One of the most important duties of the Steering Committee is to create an aim for the organization. The aim is a concise statement of the purpose (or mission) of the enterprise, the long term objective (or vision), and the guiding principles (or values). The aim is usually no more than one page in length, written in understandable language. Creating a suitable aim is more than the product of a weekend management retreat. It is very carefully constructed as the guiding strategy for the enterprise.

The Steering Committee also develops a system of metrics, linked directly to measuring progress toward accomplishing the aim. The system of metrics can be thought of as a gauge of progress. And, when processes are stable and process behavior charts are employed, we have a reasonable indication of the future—metrics provide the Steering Committee a predictive tool.

The Steering Committee is faced with four fairly simple questions on a daily basis:

1. How are we doing?
2. What are we going to do now?
3. How will we do it?
4. And, how will we know when we have accomplished what we have set out to do?

The answers to these questions operationally define the enterprise. The aim and system of metrics provide the method to answer these questions and the benchmark to measure success.

No one metric is sufficient by itself. The metrics are established as a system—a comprehensive set to be used together, not individually. The system of metrics is balanced to measure all aspects of enterprise performance. It contains measurements of internal and external performance, including customer satisfaction measurements. Metrics track historical performance and provide to the Steering Committee a comprehensive picture of the current status of the organization, a record of where it has been in the past, and a reasonable indication of where it will be in the future.

Indications of future behavior may be obtained from process behavior charts. The three-sigma limits on the chart define what a predictable process will produce, and they also approximate that level of performance that we could achieve if we learned how to manage an unpredictable process in a predictable manner. This characterization of actual or potential process performance is an important management tool.

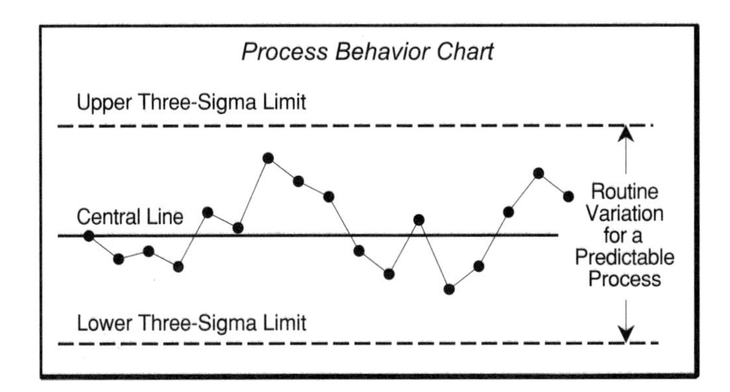


This process behavior chart displays routine variation, indicating that the process is subject only to the effects of *common* causes, and is therefore likely to be predictable in the future, operating within the three-sigma limits.

The system of metrics becomes vital to the Steering Committee in the fulfillment of their duties. When we compare stable process behavior with desired performance we have an immediate indication of our level of achievement. When we identify an area where our performance falls short we can assign a *PPI* team to find solutions for improving this aspect of our performance. If, on the other hand, our process behavior chart indicates that special causes of variation are at work (a point or points outside the lines), we can find and fix the dominant cause(s). Metrics displayed on process behavior charts tell us how we are doing. And when we are not doing so well they provide an indication of what we should do about it.

The Steering Committee provides leadership to the *PPI* program. (Remember, management buy-in is insufficient—involvement is required.) The Committee's primary responsibility is to review progress toward near-term success as well as the long-term aim. They are also responsible for integrating *PPI* into the fabric of the organization and the success of the *PPI* program, including training, projects, and success of the *PPI* teams.

Members of the Steering Committee have individual responsibilities and they are involved in *PPI* activities within their areas of responsibility. They are careful to guide and coach their people, not steer them to preconceived solutions. The Steering Committee approves all team solutions and they actively monitor implementation and ongoing control plans.

The Steering Committee appoints people to the following organizational positions. (None of them are full time; new people to manage the *PPI* program are unnecessary.) None of these positions are voluntary except Facilitators.

## Program Champion

This position is normally filled by a senior manager in the organization, usually the CEO, COO, or a functional vice president. This person is responsible for successful administration of the program. If there are enterprise segments such as divisions it is appropriate to assign program champions for administration of activities at those levels as well.

## Program Coordinators

These managers are responsible for day-to-day management of *PPI* activities. Primary duties include coordinating activities of the Steering Committee, coordinating resources, training, scheduling, and team assignment, following up on team implementation and control plans, and managing resources. This position is normally filled by a director-level manager.

## Program Administrators

These people shadow the Program Coordinators and are responsible for schedules, administrative coordination, and materials. Program Administrators care for the details of the *PPI* program in support of management activities.

## Process Champions

All managers in the enterprise serve as Process Champions for teams in their area of responsibility.* In the beginning they are assigned to *PPI* projects by the Steering Committee. As the program matures managers assume responsibility on their own to start and champion *PPI* teams. They are responsible for their *PPI* teams' success. Once the solutions and recommendations of their teams are approved by the Steering Committee, Process Champions are responsible for implementation and control, just as they are responsible for implementing any change in a process under their purview. Process Champions shoulder a significant amount of responsibility. They are careful not to steer the team to a predetermined solution, rather they coach, guide, and break down barriers so that the team is successful.

## Facilitators

These people are trained to *actively* engage the teams as they pursue process improvements using The Eight Step Method. They are responsible for coaching the team through The Eight Step Method, freeing members to concentrate on their project. They attend every team meeting. They actively coach the team to meet project milestones, working with the Process Champion to ensure the team remains engaged and on track. They are not passive observers. They retain advanced knowledge and expertise regarding

---

* It has been common for managers to "opt out" of programs like *PPI*. This is not an option with *PPI*. All managers are involved. Those choosing not to become engaged as Process Champions are considered to have opted out of the enterprise. Participation is not voluntary.

deployment and application of *PPI* methods and tools. Each Facilitator need not be expert in all of the statistical tools, however. Facilitators are part of a team, providing each other assistance when required. Facilitators are volunteers, because of the nature of what they do and the intensity of their work. (The position of Facilitator is the only volunteer position within the *PPI* program.)

## Summary

In this chapter we have discussed the *PPI* organization and support system and the duties and responsibilities of people therein. In the next chapter we will discuss the interactions within the team process improvement model.[*]

[*] For a more in-depth discussion of the *PPI* organization and management duties and responsibilities read *Practical Process Improvement Managers Guide* by this author available from SPC Press, Knoxville.

# Chapter Eight

# The *PPI* Team Model

As mentioned in the introduction, a preeminent goal in developing Practical Process Improvement was to establish a single consistent program. We have done this by establishing a set of rules. This chapter describes the team process improvement model in the context of two fundamental principles, seven general rules, and six guidelines for project selection and team deployment.

## Two Fundamental Principles

### I. The source of *PPI* projects is the enterprise aim.

*PPI* projects are linked to the enterprise aim through the system of metrics. The Steering Committee conducts periodic operational reviews, the centerpiece of which is a review of the system of metrics. *PPI* teams are identified to improve performance shortfalls. By using the system of metrics as the source of *PPI* projects we take the guesswork out of project selection. The selection is driven by data.

### II. *PPI* projects further the enterprise aim.

The system of metrics is developed specifically to measure progress toward the enterprise aim. So, when teams address performance shortfalls they are furthering achievement of the aim.

Enterprise level metrics that link the team project to the enterprise aim are written out for the team at the time of project selection. They are provided to the team at the beginning of the team project. The team should not have to guess at the enterprise level metric(s) that prompted their formation.

## Seven General Rules

**1. Identify Financial Impact.**

*PPI* project teams will normally identify a financial impact from their solutions. It is not prudent to conduct an ROI predetermination of the team's financial contribution. While it is possible to determine potential savings ahead of time, predicting precise financial results is not possible. It will only be possible to determine the financial contribution after the solutions are found. Methods developed to assess financial impact earlier are simply snake oil. *PPI* teams measure the financial impact of their project when they know the solutions to the problems they were given.

**2. Provide Steering Committee Coordination and Guidance.**

The Steering Committee is ultimately responsible for coordinating *PPI* activities and providing guidance regarding program administration. In practice, the Steering Committee is involved in more details early in the program and less as the program matures. The Program Coordinator is the primary advisor to the Steering Committee. He or she ensures that the Steering Committee has necessary data and knowledge to accomplish the program objectives. The Program Coordinator is the conduit for information flow from the Steering Committee to Process Champions, Facilitators, managers, and *PPI* project teams.

**3. Focus the Project Scope.**

It is not prudent to expect a *PPI* team to take on an enterprise-wide project aimed at correcting all causes of metrics shortfalls. Rather, the optimum method for selecting a project begins with identifying key shortfalls. The shortfalls are then prioritized within the context of the near-term goals and objectives. These opportunities are then melded into other priorities to develop a list of prioritized *PPI* projects. From the list of prioritized projects, specific projects are selected and scheduled. Then a problem statement is derived for each project, usually to address the most significant area or component of the shortfall.

For example, we have a shortfall in on-time delivery. We are currently achieving only 80% on-time delivery for all product lines. We decide to assign this problem to a *PPI* team. It is appropriate for the Steering Committee, or Process Champion, to conduct a preliminary analysis from available data in order to determine the product or product lines that are in the worst shape.

By narrowing down the project scope to a specific product, we will be more successful than by trying to tackle the entire problem. The team will be able to complete their project in a short amount of time (six to twelve weeks) so we will begin to see improvement right away. And by solving the problem for a product or product line, we often find that the solutions apply to the great majority of other product lines.

**4. State the Problem Concisely and Appropriately.**

One of the Process Champion's primary tasks is to create a concise problem statement—a key component of the project mission statement—that defines the problem assigned to the team.

It is never appropriate to assign a project with predetermined causes, solutions, or problem statements for which there is only one solution. If the cause of the problem is known, then it should be a relatively simple matter to find the solution. This is a job for the process area manager. If the solution is already known, a good manager will simply implement it. If there is only one solution, then once again, it is a job for the process area manager.

We assign a *PPI* team only to a problem when we do not know the solution. When the solution is known good managers implement that solution. It is not cost effective to assign a *PPI* team as an "implementation" team. A *PPI* team works best when it concentrates on finding the solutions to a problem, removing waste, improving processes, and improving customer satisfaction.

### Appropriate Problem Statements

1. Manufacturing cycle time is too long.
2. We are unable to deliver to our customers on time.
3. It takes too long to process a customer order.
4. We cannot track products through the assembly process.
5. Sub-assembly yield is too low.

### Inappropriate Problem Statements

1. Supplier delays are causing slow cycle times.
2. Manufacturing cycle time is causing late deliveries.
3. Customer order processing is not automated.
4. We do not have a barcode tracking system.
5. People are making mistakes in sub-assembly

Above are some examples of appropriate problem statements and corresponding examples of inappropriate problem statements. Note the short, concise nature of the appropriate statements without hint of a preconceived solution. While the inappropriate problem statements are short and concise, they infer (or state) either a solution, cause, or source of the problem.

**5. Create a Definite Project Schedule.**

Establishing a clear and concise schedule for project completion is an important step during project definition. In addition to begin and end dates, the schedule shows training dates and interim milestones. Clearly defined guidelines are established, including the percentage of time team members may devote to the project, and when the project will be completed (a deadline). The specific team meeting schedules are established later by the team, using these guidelines.

**6. Assign an Appropriate Project Facilitator.**

A Facilitator is selected jointly by the Process Champion and the Program Coordinator. There is a human tendency to become "comfortable" working with certain people and to request the same Facilitator over and over again. This could result in Facilitator overload. The Program Coordinator ensures that the Facilitator load is shared evenly.

There have been some rules in other programs that prevent Facilitators from working with teams on processes in which they have subject matter knowledge. *PPI* contains no such rules. There is no valid reason to exclude Facilitators from working with teams just because they know something about the subject matter at hand. *PPI* Facilitators are trained to be objective and to separate themselves from project decisions. Their job is to facilitate the team process. In practice we actually find times when Facilitators have an advantage working with teams in their area of responsibility. They can provide expert assistance and details of process operations, and their credibility is enhanced because they have subject area knowledge.

**7. Select Four to Eight Team Members**

The Process Champion and the Facilitator normally confer and select a Team Leader. The Team Leader is someone with fairly complete knowledge of the process, some recognized natural leadership ability, and who is a respected member of the organization. The Team Leader is the administrator and official point of contact for the team. The Team Leader is not the "boss" of the team and never steers the team toward a solution.

The Process Champion, Facilitator, and Team Leader may then proceed to team member selection. *PPI* teams normally include between six and eight members in addition to the Process Champion and Facilitator, but never fewer than four members. Team members are selected because of their knowledge, skills, and their ability to contribute to the project. Team members are *never* selected to fulfill a training requirement or a quota.

## Guidelines for Effective Projects

- Primary stakeholders should be identified early and they should agree on the importance of the project. Stakeholders normally include customers, managers, people in the process, and suppliers.
- The project should be easily defined and should have fairly narrow boundaries. Potential boundaries are identified by the Process Champion and always include the process start (a specific step or event) and the process end. Boundaries may also include things like:

1. geographic boundaries, such as domestic only or European only;
2. a specific product or product line;
3. a specific region or plant;
4. a defined time frame (i.e., changes were made recently and examination of previous data would be counter-productive); and
5. others as appropriate to the specific project.

- Do not select a project being worked on by another team (for obvious reasons).
- The process should not be undergoing a major change.
- Do not pick a project for political reasons or to steer a team to conclusions for an ulterior aim. This motive quickly becomes apparent and demoralizes everyone.
- Finally, processes that occur infrequently are difficult to improve and improvements are normally difficult to test. These processes are not inappropriate project candidates, but the difficulties should be recognized up front.

## Characteristics of a Good *PPI* Project

- It is important to the enterprise, as reflected in an important key business metric.
- It is important to stakeholders: customers, management, people in the process, suppliers.
- It is simple with definable and narrow boundaries.

## Cautions

- If a solution is predetermined, the project *will* be a disaster.
- Every effort should be made to involve the people in the process being improved.

***Project Selection Checklist***

- ☐ The project is targeted to improve the following company level metric(s):

  ________________ ________________

  ________________ ________________
- ☐ Primary stakeholders have been identified and concur with the project definition. There is general agreement that the project is important.
- ☐ The process is not undergoing change nor is it in transition.
- ☐ A clear and concise problem statement has been developed.
- ☐ There is not a predetermined solution.
- ☐ Preliminary process boundaries have been identified.
- ☐ It will be fairly simple and straightforward for the team to flowchart the process within the boundaries.
- ☐ The process completes its cycle frequently.
- ☐ The process is not being worked on by another team.

## A Review of Team Roles

Once the project definition is completed and team composition is decided it is time to begin the project. This begins with a preliminary meeting, no more than thirty minutes, in which the Process Champion reviews the project problem statement, including the boundaries, project schedule, and other team guidelines. Questions are encouraged in order to prevent downstream ambiguities. At this first meeting, it is appropriate to identify and clearly define team roles.

### Process Champion

- Is responsible for the team's success
- Defines the project including preliminary boundaries
- Provides resources and administrative guidelines
- Reviews progress regularly
- Breaks down barriers
- Responsible for implementing team solutions

### Team Leader

- Manages the administration of the team
- Provides leadership as required
- Serves as the official team point of contact
- Retains official records
- Assists the Process Champion during implementation

### Facilitator

- Focuses on the team process, allowing the team to concentrate on the project
- Teaches, coaches, and facilitates team progress
- Keeps the team moving
- Provides interim leadership as required
- Helps prepare reports to management
- Is careful to prevent anyone steering the team to a solution

### Team Members

- Participate fully in meetings
- Complete assignments and sub-team activities on time
- Come to team meetings fully prepared
- Support the team leader, lend assistance to teammates

### Other Team Roles

- Timekeeper: keeps the team on agenda
- Scribe: keeps official records (agenda and minutes)
- Recorder: during the meetings records team ideas on a flip chart (all team work utilizes flip charts—a visual reference)
- Spokesperson: presents team reports to management

## Conducting a *PPI* Project

The time frame for completing *PPI* projects is managed carefully, and takes between six and twelve weeks—normally twelve weeks in the beginning, moving to six weeks or less as the program matures. During program roll out (the training phase), the duration depends on scheduling. There are seven formal training days. If the formal training is scheduled every other week, the project will complete in twelve weeks. If the formal training is scheduled every week, the project will complete in six weeks.

As the program matures everyone in the enterprise will have eventually completed the team training. Then, when training is no longer required, the projects will complete in six weeks or fewer.

Teams are normally allotted time for two 2-hour formal meetings per week during the project in addition to formal training time. The formal meetings are crisp, reserved for planning, data review, analysis, and decision making. Data gathering and other time-consuming work is accomplished outside of the formal meetings.

A short team deadline provides creative tension—a stretch goal (technically, facilitating anxiety). Teams are able to meet the time goals by using The Eight Step Method.

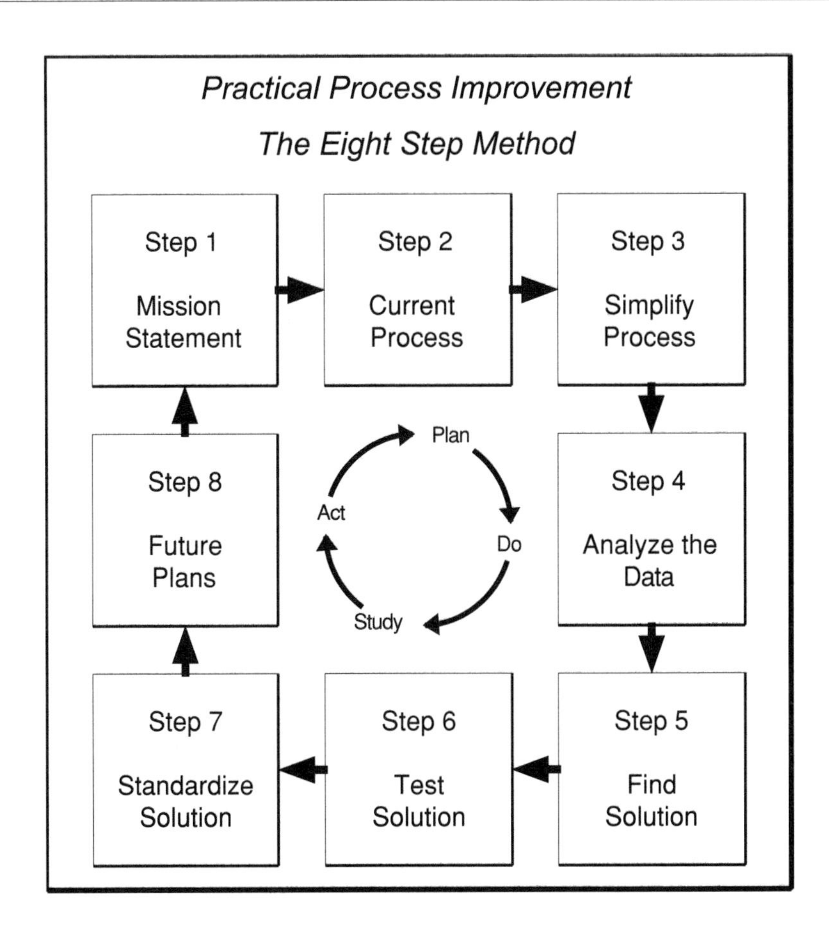


## The Eight Step Method

The Eight Step Method is the standard for *PPI* team projects. Based on the PDSA model, it ensures that :

1. the team achieves meaningful results,
2. the team is able to support its solutions and recommendations with data,
3. solutions are tested prior to implementation, and
4. all team projects conform to a standard process throughout the enterprise.

## Step One – Mission Statement

- Identify the problem or gap and its importance
- Define the process and project boundaries
- Develop metrics
- Identify stakeholders, their needs and concerns

*Example of a Mission Statement*

**Problem:**
*Currently, cycle time for order entry is too long (10 days):*

**Results of Problem:**
*Resulting in production delays and late deliveries.*

**Desired State / Goal (Customer Requirement):**
*Our desired state is to complete the order entry process in less than three days and achieve this goal within 3 month.*

**Process Boundaries:**
*Our process begins when the customer order is received in customer service and logged in and ends with key entry RP-12 signifying completion of order entry into the ERP system.*

**Metrics:**

1) Company level metrics:
   *Customer Allegiance, On-Time Delivery*
2) Team metrics:
   a) In Process metrics:
      *Waiting time for orders in the process,*
      *orders per month, number of orders that are delayed, reasons for delays.*
   b) Output metric: *Cycle Time of Order Entry*

## Step Two – Current Process

- Understand the history
- Completely describe what is currently happening
- Flowchart the current process with times for each step, begin with a "30,000 ft" overview and then in detail
- Identify key process steps
- Use other useful information
- Begin gathering data

## Step Three – Simplify the Process

- Look for quick fixes in the detailed flowchart
- Look for obvious problems
- Remove all obvious waste and problems

## Step Four – Analyze the Data

- Construct a cause and effect diagram
- Identify possible causes
- Use other tools as necessary to isolate problems
- Use statistical tools to define process performance and reduce process variation

## Step Five – Find Solutions

- Find solutions using data and analysis from Step Four
- Identify stakeholders, keep them informed
- Identify barriers, work with Process Champion to overcome them
- Develop a plan to test solutions

## Step Six – Test Solutions

- Conduct a test of solutions using the PDSA model
  - Plan the test
  - Conduct the test
  - Study the results of the test
  - Take appropriate action based on the results of the test
- It may be necessary to return to Step Four if solutions do not work

## Step Seven – Standardization

- Describe the new process
- Develop a detailed plan to implement and control all improvements
- Assign dates and people responsible to all action items
- Implement all improvements
- Ensure a control plan is in place to hold the gains (a process behavior chart for the team's ourput metric is the principal instrument for monitoring and control)

## Step Eight – Future Plans

- Review discovered items outside team boundaries
- List all items beyond the scope of the team that should be addressed by management
- Decide if the team needs to tackle a new project, work another round on this one, or close out
- Make recommendations for future, related *PPI* teams

## Reporting, Implementation, and Control

In this section we will discuss team reporting requirements, approval of team solutions, and implementation and control—what happens after the *PPI* team completes training and/or their discovery work and have found their solutions. While teams work independently, management involvement and oversight is crucial.

### Reporting On the Project

Reporting requirements are integral to the *PPI* process. The purpose of the reports is to provide updates, gain approval of interim activities, provide a final report of the team's accomplishments, and gain approval of solutions.

Interim reports are provided to the Process Champion as required, at a minimum:

- for approval of the mission statement, primarily the goal and process boundaries
- after Step Three, before implementing quick fixes
- after Step Four to review the team's data and analysis for completeness
- after Step Five to review the potential solutions and the test plan
- after Step Six to review the test results, before preparing the Implementation and Control Plan.

At the end of their project, every *PPI* team presents a formal "Report-Out" to the Steering Committee. The Report-Out provides continuity from discovery and solutions to implementation and control. It signals the end of training. The Report-Out is presented to the Steering Committee, stakeholders, people who have been assigned action items, and other people as required. The Report-Out is a public event.

The Report-Out is scheduled during team formation—up front. It is a deadline that the teams must meet; a milestone marking the transition to the Process Champion responsibility for implementation and control. Team involvement after the Report-Out will vary depending on progress and future plans.

The objective is to complete the project prior to the Report-Out. However, each team is different, we never create a race to accomplishment, and some teams may not have completely finished their project. In every case, however, the Report-Out will contain a thorough review of the project, progress to date, and a *complete* list of actions required for implementation.

## Implementation Phase of Project

The Implementation and Control plan is a detailed spreadsheet of *all* actions required:

1. to complete all remaining project work,
2. to complete all testing activities, and
3. to complete implementation of all solutions including documentation, training, data collection, and control.

The Implementation and Control plan need not be a complex spreadsheet but it does need to be a detailed spreadsheet. It is a thorough and complete listing of all required actions, assigning specific responsibility, start date, and completion date. The plan includes details of establishing the output metric to monitor and control the process in the future.

The plan operationally defines the process improvement solutions. It answers the following questions: What do you want to accomplish? By what method are you going to accomplish it? How will you know when it has been accomplished?

The Process Champion is responsible for managing the completion of the Implementation and Control plan. The *PPI* team leader and team members may be employed as required during implementation. However, implementation actions are seldom limited solely to members of the team. Other stakeholders are employed as required. This is one of the primary reasons that implementation is a management function, not a team function. The Process Champion has the clout to get things done, remove obstacles and barriers, and to assign responsibility and accountability.

Until all actions are completed, the Process Champion reports the status of the Implementation and Control plan to the Steering Committee monthly.

## Control Phase of Project

One of the most important team activities is creation of an output metric to measure accomplishment of the goal. The team usually begins charting this metric in the third or fourth week of the project. The output metric is linked directly to the team goal and is used as the primary indicator of team success. The output metric chart is the primary tool that the Process Champion uses to monitor and control the performance of the improved process.

| *Examples of Team Output Metrics* | |
|---|---|
| *Goal* | *Output Metric* |
| Reduce work cell cycle time | Work cell cycle time |
| Reduce WIP inventory | WIP inventory |
| Increase end of line yield | First pass yield |
| Decrease billing errors | % of returned invoices |

## *Output Metric Chart Example*

Duration of Discrepant Material Awaiting Return to Supplier
Sample Implementation and Control Plan Format

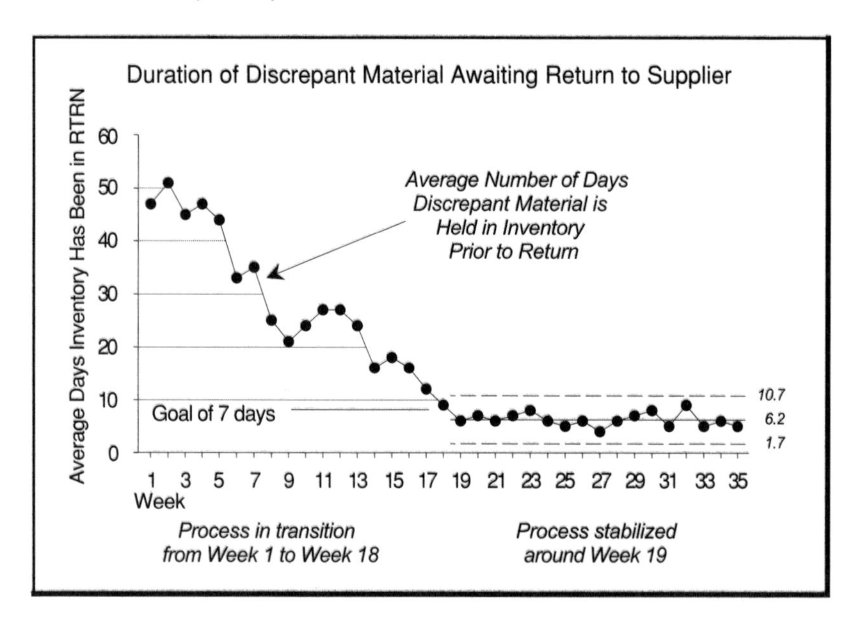


Goal: Reduce duration of inventory awaiting disposition from over 45 days to 7 days

It can be seen from the chart of the output metric that the team met their goal. The process appears to have stabilized at an average of 6.2 days, having been reduced from over 45 days. Since the objective was to change the current system, it was sufficient initially to track progress using a simple run chart. As the process began to stabilize it was appropriate to convert the running record into a process behavior chart. This chart defines the current state of the process, defines what you can expect in the future, and shows in a timely manner any unintentional process changes that may occur in the future. Output metric charts such as these are monitored by the Process Champion and the Steering Committee for at least six months after the Report-Out.

## Summary

The Practical Process Improvement team model provides structure, methods, and tools for employee teams to tackle a broad range of improvement projects. These projects are not limited only to "production" or "operations" projects. The model applies equally to all processes of production: order administration, customer service, finance, human resources, and all other enterprise processes.

# Chapter Nine

# The *PPI* Training Process

This chapter discusses the Practical Process Improvement training process and its underlying training methodology. Training is primarily conducted during program implementation and is segmented into seminars and team training. The seminars are short training sessions for managers and facilitators. The team training is linked with project teams and conducted simultaneously with the roll out of the first *PPI* projects.

All training discussed in this chapter is required training. Each training seminar or session is a one-time event. Once completed the participants are qualified for that skill set.

The *PPI* training discussed in this chapter is basic. Because the application of more advanced tools is open-ended within the *PPI* model, further training may be required for specific people to gain specific skills. For example, additional training in statistical methods or advanced tools may be required for selected people who need to become skilled in those particular methods or tools. We do not attempt to make everyone an expert in all facets of *PPI*, nor do we create cadres of experts or exclusive clubs of quality professionals. We do train people, as required, in specific advanced tools and skills to act as consultants for the teams.

## Managers Seminar

Two days in duration, the managers seminar provides enterprise leaders with an overview of the *PPI* theory, methods, processes, and their duties and responsibilities. The Managers Seminar is conducted prior to any of the other training.

## Facilitators Seminar

Four days in duration, the Facilitators Seminar provides Facilitators with the basic knowledge and skills to fulfill their duties and responsibilities. Facilitators should be trained about two weeks before the first team training event.

## *PPI* Team Training

Seven training days, spread over a six to twelve week period, provides everyone in the enterprise the basic knowledge, skills, and tools to successfully complete *PPI* projects.

Team training is the fundamental basis for imparting knowledge and skills to everyone in the organization. Initially four or five teams meet together for their training in how to use The Eight Step Method to carry out a *PPI* project. Training multiple teams simultaneously expedites the training process and facilitates inter-team and organizational learning. This training is carefully structured to provide the skills, tools, and methods *at the time the team members will be putting them to use.* This approach ensures maximum retention.

The diagram on the next page provides an overview of *PPI*

training and project integration. There are four phases:

- Phase One, the training phase, is only appropriate during program implementation.
- Once people are trained in The Eight Step Method teams begin directly with Phase Two, the project phase.
- Phases Three and Four, implementation and control, are under direction of the Process Champion.

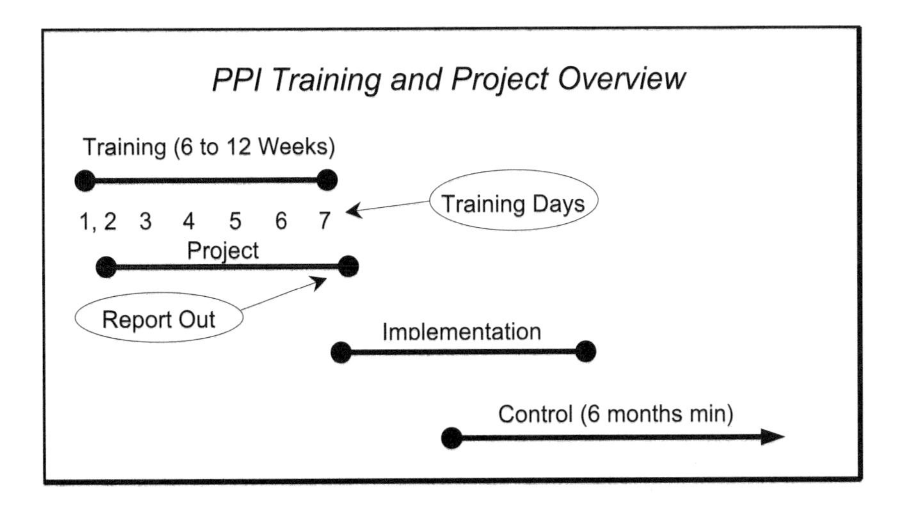


As you can see in the diagram above, training and project work are conducted simultaneously. During the training phase the team's efforts are coordinated with the training syllabus. The duration of the initial projects will depend upon the frequency of training. There are seven formal training days. If the formal training is scheduled every other week the project will complete in twelve weeks. If the formal training is scheduled every week the project will complete in six weeks. Once training is complete (and everyone is trained) the teams will operate independently and projects will typically complete in six weeks.

Training and project work follows the following schedule. Days One and Two are back to back in the first week of the project, while the remaining five days are spread out over the next five to eleven weeks.

*PPI* Training Schedule

| ***Training Day*** | ***Training Topics*** | ***Project Work The Eight Step Method*** |
|---|---|---|
| 1 | *PPI* Overview Concepts, & Methods | 1. Mission Statement |
| 2 | *PPI* Basic Tools & The Eight Step Method | 2. Current Process<br>3. Simplification |
| 3 | *PPI* Statistical Tools | Review completed Steps 1-3<br>Begin Step 4. Analyze Data |
| 4 to 6 | Progress reviews<br>Training on selected topics as required | 4. Analyze the Data<br>5. Find Solutions<br>6. Test the solutions<br>7. Standardization<br>8. Future Plans |
| 7 | Dress Rehearsal | Rehearse Report Out |

The first day of training includes an overview of the *PPI* program, the team process, and the concepts and methods of team improvement projects. Project work begins on the first day of training with Step One of The Eight Step Method as the team fleshes out their problem statement and then, in turn, develops a mission statement.

On the second day the training gets more specific with guidance on conducting a team project, following The Eight Step Method, and the *PPI* basic tools. The teams begin work on Step

Two of The Eight Step Method (Define the Current Process) by starting to construct their basic process flowcharts.

| *PPI Basic Tools* | *PPI Statistical Tools* |
| --- | --- |
| Meetings | Run charts |
| Brainstorming | Process Behavior Charts |
| Quick Vote | Histograms |
| Check Sheet | Scatter diagrams |
| Pareto Chart | |
| Flowcharts | |
| Fishbone Diagram | |
| Other tools as needed | |

Between the second and third training day the team completes Step Two (Define the Current Process) and Step Three (Simplify the Current Process). The first event of the third training day is a progress review involving all teams in the training cycle and the instructor, who in turn, provides feedback and coaching. These progress reviews become a major tool for organizational learning. The sharing of knowledge and skills between the individuals and the teams that occurs in these reviews is one of the most powerful benefits of the *PPI* program. The remainder of the third training day is devoted to training in the *PPI* statistical tools.

Project work, progress reviews, and training (as required) continue simultaneously until the seventh training day. This is the rehearsal day for the teams' report-outs at which they will summarize their project work in a formal presentation.

## Training Methodology

*PPI* is designed to involve everyone. It is not centered on a few highly trained individuals who are responsible for productivity and quality improvement. All people are resources and everyone is involved in the activities to improve profitability.

How do we accomplish this? For the answer we turn to the practical, day-to-day application of modern concepts of adult learning. *PPI* utilizes three adult learning models—behavioral, humanist, and cognitive. All three are incorporated in the structure, materials, and delivery of the *PPI* syllabus, as well as day-to-day management of the program.

| *Adult Learning Models* | |
|---|---|
| Behavioral Model | Learning as a change of behavior |
| Humanist Model | Learning as emotional well being |
| Cognitive Model | Learning as an active and constructive internal mental process that cannot be directly observed |

## The Behavioral Model

*The behavioral learning model proposes that learning may be defined as a change in observable, physical behavior.* We can assume people have learned something when their behavior changes appropriately, reflecting the new learning. This model relies on the belief that people respond to stimulus, positive or negative, and that behavior modification gives evidence of learning. One of the best ways to change behavior is through rewards. In this model, learning is a matter of conditioning—reward positive behavior, ignore (or discipline) inappropriate behavior. Learning by association is also a powerful form of conditioning.

*PPI* incorporates the behavioral learning model in the following ways. Rewards are appropriate when they are non-competitive and directed at improving team efforts. Behaviorists suggest implementing new changes gradually, especially if there is resistance. We allow reasonable and incremental progress. Teams need not make a "breakthrough" with each endeavor. This is consistent with proven results. As Dr. Wheeler points out, "...one can rarely leap from current conditions to the ultimate process potential." *

One of the more powerful aspects of the behavioral model is learning by association. That is why *PPI* emphasizes that managers and leaders must model intended behavior—practice what you preach, walk the talk. People in the *PPI* program will be no more enthusiastic about it than their leader.

In the behavioral model there is a direct link between behavior and learning. It is important, therefore, to put new information to immediate use to reinforce the new learning. For example, a new tool taught in an abstract way will be easily forgotten. If that same tool is put to immediate use, however, it will be easily remembered and will be understood in the appropriate context. That is why the *PPI* training is presented just in time. The new concepts, methods, skills, and tools are presented at the appropriate time for people to put them to immediate use, in a team environment, on a problem in which they are familiar.

---

* *Understanding Statistical Process Control, Second Edition*, Donald J. Wheeler and David S. Chambers, SPC Press, Knoxville, p. 152.

There are some cautions when applying the behavioral model. People's behavior may indicate that learning has occurred, but people may not have changed how they think or feel. If we concentrate on behavior only we may miss important signals that people may not understand or care how or why the new behaviors are necessary or effective. Further, if our program is based only on rewards, desired behavior may vanish if those rewards are not forthcoming. In a worst case scenario, excessive use of rewards may lead to people relying on rewards as their only stimulus to work. And once rewards are introduced people will come to expect them, and they will expect more over time. For these reasons, rewards are used sparingly in *PPI*. Teams or individuals are not rewarded monetarily for completing a project nor are they conditioned to believe that they will share the savings from their productivity efforts. The objective is to develop intrinsic (internal) motivation within each employee so that all may succeed together.

## The Humanist Model

*The humanist model of learning proposes that consideration for emotional well being is the key to successful learning*. The focus is on cultural and emotional considerations. The objective is to create a positive, nurturing, non-threatening environment in which people can learn and flourish. In the extreme, humanists hold that we need only to create the necessary cultural environment and appropriate learning will follow.

Humanists' primary considerations are for the emotional dimension of the people in the enterprise. Aspects of the humanists' view include an appreciation of the emotional responses: anxiety (fear of the unknown), self esteem, risk-taking, empathy, and motivation. Anxiety may be positive or negative—facilitative or debilitative—depending on how the new learning or goals are presented. Self esteem and risk taking are closely related considerations that depend on people's comfort with the new scenario.

Among other dimensions of motivation, there are two primary types: extrinsic motivation (caused by external stimulus) and intrinsic motivation (caused by an internal drive to succeed or learn). Extrinsic motivation is very closely linked to behavioral learning. However, humanists hold that ultimately, a person's commitment to any endeavor is a culmination of their level of anxiety, self-esteem, risk-taking, motivation and empathy. Motivation is the culmination of all the emotional elements and comes from within.

*PPI* incorporates the humanist learning model in the following ways. Anxiety (fear of the unknown) is mitigated through open and honest communication based on clear and commonly understood concepts and information. Risk taking is mitigated by carefully presenting new concepts, skills, and information in ways that are easily understood by people of all educational and cultural backgrounds.

When people are thrust into situations where they believe they will fail, debilitating anxiety is created—a very strong de-motivator. People simply quit trying. (In extreme situations a person may shut down; become paralyzed mentally and/or physically.

Therefore, *PPI* creates situations where people may succeed. We are careful, for example, not to force people to learn beyond their capability when teaching statistical tools. It is sufficient for one or two people on each team to have a grasp of the more complex tools.

On the other hand, when we create situations where people may succeed but only with significant effort, we create facilitating anxiety, a powerful motivator. Facilitating anxiety stimulates motivation to accomplish a worthwhile goal. With facilitating anxiety people know that the goal is difficult but achievable. We call these stretch goals. Completion of team projects within the six to twelve week time frame is a stretch-goal built into the *PPI* program. Team improvement goals are the other stretch-goals promoted within the *PPI* program. Process Champions work with the teams to establish appropriate improvement goals. An improvement goal creates facilitating anxiety when the team recognizes its difficulty but know they can achieve it through hard work. In creating stretch-goals, great care is in order so that the motivation does not cross the threshold from facilitating to debilitating anxiety.

A precondition for a successful *PPI* program is the creation of an environment where people are free to learn and take pride in their work. We call this a learning environment. Other efforts will be futile until this environment is created. However, merely creating this environment will most likely not result in improved profitability. Improving processes and profits is hard work. "Feel-good" efforts alone are insufficient.

*PPI* is not about team building; rather, *PPI* is aimed at improving enterprise profitability through cost reduction and improving customer satisfaction. But the cultural benefit of team excellence is a nice bonus, a byproduct managed carefully within the *PPI* program. We do not rely on team building to improve profitability but we recognize the necessity and positive benefits of a learning environment, where teamwork is the norm. *It cannot be overemphasized that until a learning environment is in place, efforts to es-*

*tablish a viable PPI program will fail.*

There are some cautions within the emotional dimension. People may develop an increased commitment to doing well but may not change the way they think about or do their work. Positive attitudes do not always result in improvement that is measurable or meaningful. There are examples of teams formed for team-building alone where the results actually cost the enterprise money and/or valuable time. To reiterate, a learning environment (a safe, nurturing culture) is required but alone it is insufficient to bring about meaningful improvement.

## The Cognitive Model

*The cognitive model proposes that learning involves mental processes that are not directly observable. Adult learning is based on relating new information to what we already know.* The cognitive model of learning is the most modern of the three. It is not only a model of learning but it is also a model of managing people and designing systems intended to increase productivity, such as computer-aided design and administrative software.

The cognitive learning model is based on the notion that we organize our knowledge according to structures known as schemas or schemata. Based on things we have learned in the past, we, as adults, retain schemata in our neo-cortex (gray matter), These schemata are alternatively referred to as paradigms, mental models, or theories. Each schema is placed and arranged in our brain much as files are arranged on a computer screen or in a file cabinet. When we are presented with new information our brain immediately looks for somewhere to file it—to attach it to our existing filing system.

According to the cognitive model learning occurs as follows:

- We receive information
- We process it, based on existing schemata
- Learning and understanding occur when new information is successfully attached to an existing schema. Until it is attached it is merely memorized by rote.

Failure to learn is due to our inability to successfully attach the new information to an existing schema. We may certainly "memorize" the new information, but memorized information is perishable, easily forgotten. Inability to learn may also be due to the way new information is presented, i.e., insufficient clues are offered or existing paradigms or norms act as filters to prevent attachment of the new information.

So within the *PPI* syllabus, and all other elements of the program, we go to great lengths to ensure new information is presented in the context of existing knowledge. When people do not understand what we are trying to teach them we ask the question, "Will you help me understand how you understood what I said so that I may understand why you are having difficulty?" We recognize that information memorized by rote is easily and surely forgotten. Information attached to an existing schema is easily remembered.

The first step in helping people understand new information is to determine what they already know. Then we can explain new information in that context, in understandable ways. The *PPI* syllabus uses plenty of clear examples, pictures, and stories. During seminars, team training sessions, progress reviews, town hall meetings, planning meetings, etc., new information is explained not only in content but also the context. Key points are repeated often. Every available opportunity is taken to reinforce the most important aspects of the strategy for improving profit.

In previous chapters we have used the term "operational definitions" in various contexts. Operational definitions help us develop a way to think about issues and problems. They enhance our ability to attached new information to an existing schema by answering three questions about what is being defined. *What do you want to accomplish? By what method are you going to accomplish it? How will you know when it has been accomplished?*

## Operational Definitions

Operational definitions provide the bases for effective communication. They provide a reasonable definition of what is to be accomplished including a method and a way to interpret the results of our efforts. An operational definition contains the following essential elements:

- A definition of what is to be accomplished; a definition upon which reasonable people can agree. This is what we hope to achieve.
- A methodology to employ. This will include methods, techniques, and tools to deliver what we hope to achieve.
- A way to know if we have accomplished what we hoped to achieve and what further action is required. Operational definitions include a way to measure our progress; a way to interpret the data and make a judgment.

You will recall that this is the same concept we used earlier in our discussions of Implementation and Control plans. The Implementation and Control plan is an operational definition of our process improvement plan. Operational definitions may be simple or complex. They may be stated in a few words, a document, as numbers, or in any of a variety of other ways. *They always, however, answer the three questions. What do you want to accomplish? By what method are you going to accomplish it? How will you know when it has been accomplished?* Moreover, operational definitions define things in ways that we can understand and file away in our system of schemata. They become the common understanding of the way we do business.

## Examples of Operational Definitions

- An enterprise mission and vision statement is an operational definition when it answers the *three* questions: what the enterprise wants to accomplish (the aim), the methodology (Practical Process Improvement or something similar), and a set of criteria to measure and judge progress (the system of metrics).
- A *PPI* team mission statement operationally defines the team project: the problem statement defines what we hope to achieve; we use *PPI* as the method; and we establish a goal and an output metric to measure and interpret the results of our activities.
- A good marketing/design specification answers the *three* questions; such as, "A good automobile heater—a heater that delivers 100 degree air measured at the air duct outlet within three minutes of starting the car."
- Any properly constructed process behavior chart is an operational definition of a process. It answers the *three* questions: What do we want to accomplish? (Achieve full process potential); By what method are you going to accomplish it? (By removing exceptional variation); and, How will you know when it has been accomplished? (When the process is being operated predictably).

There are cautions with the cognitive model just as there are with the behavioral and humanist models. We must remember that people's schemata and mental models create filters that vary from person to person. These filters determine how we interpret the world—what we see and how we see it. But more importantly, they determine what we do not see. These filters are very powerful and may prevent people from understanding or correctly interpreting the new information we are trying to impart.

People all start from a different learning point. It is necessary to level the playing field, so to speak, before true organizational learning can occur. So, the first step is always to determine what people already know. This often presents difficulties because different people know different things. The objective is to get everyone in agreement at some basic level of understanding.

## Summary

Within the *PPI* training syllabus, all of these learning models are appropriately employed through technique, sequencing, and timing. All material is presented just-in-time so that it may be put to immediate use. Great care is taken to ensure that all training seminars are safe environments—people need not fear expressing thoughts and solutions. We begin each seminar with an exercise to determine what people already know, and we build upon that knowledge. We never present material in the abstract, but develop schema as we go and attach all new information to those schema so that it is retained.

Within the *PPI* program, managers use these learning models in day-to-day operations, meetings, and training programs. Key strategic initiatives are presented in understandable ways and reinforced at every opportunity. Changes are introduced in ways that make sense, and allowances are made for incremental progress over time. Managers set the example. And, foremost, great care is taken to establish and maintain a learning environment where it is okay to take risks, make mistakes, get involved, be innovative, and make improvements leading to innovation, profitable growth of the enterprise, and market leadership.

# Chapter Ten

## Getting Started

This chapter provides basic guidance on implementing a *PPI* program. It will provide a step-by-step program for getting started. It is not intended to provide every detail; it is an overview. You may find it useful to review Chapter Seven before reading further.

For a leader and/or executive team with experience in implementing and managing a quality program in the past, it will not be difficult to implement Practical Process Improvement. Following the guidelines for implementation, internal experts should be able to implement the program on their own.* However, for the uninitiated, or for those with minimal experience, it will be prudent to gain the help of a professional trainer or consultant.

Practical Process Improvement is designed to be managed by internal resources. Therefore, if you decide to seek outside assistance, find a consultant whose motive is to make you self sufficient as soon as possible. While reliance on outside assistance may be required in the beginning, a successful program will be indicated by a self sufficient management team.

There are seven basic steps in implementing a *PPI* program.

---

* This chapter is an overview. For detailed guidance refer to *Practical Process Improvement Managers Guide*, R. Edward Zunich, available from SPC Press, Knoxville.

1. Form a Steering Committee.
2. Create an Aim for the enterprise,
3. Identify key players.
4. Create a master implementation plan.
5. Develop near-term and long-term training plans.
6. Develop and conduct *PPI* projects.
7. Create processes for ongoing success.

Each of these steps will be discussed in turn.

## Form a Steering Committee

The first step in implementing Practical Process Improvement is to form a Steering Committee of senior enterprise executives. This committee should include the CEO, direct reports, and/or senior staff as well as the principal *PPI* coordinating managers. This committee will set policy and provide guidance for integrating *PPI* into the organization.

The first and most important duty of this committee is to create and deploy an aim for the organization. The aim satisfies the following requirements:

1. a statement of purpose of the enterprise (mission),
2. a longer term objective (vision),
3. a set of values to guide conduct and performance, and
4. a set of balanced metrics to judge success.

The aim is an operational definition of the enterprise answering the following questions—what do we want to do, how will we do it, and how will we know when we are successful?

Steering Committee members should have a complete grasp of the fundamentals of *PPI*. In large enterprises, there will be more than one level of executive management. At each level, steering committees should be formed, having cascading policies, guidance, strategic plans and aims, and metrics. Working through all levels of the organization, each subordinate steering committee should provide ever increasing details of *PPI* integration.

The *PPI* program requires management support. Managers at all levels must be engaged and fulfill their specific role. Without *active* management support this (or any) program will fail.

## Create an Aim for the Enterprise

The Aim of the organization may be thought of as a strategic plan. Not a marketing plan. Not a financial plan. Rather, a strategic plan in the truest sense, one that guides everyone in the enterprise towards success and market leadership.* Strategic plans that are merely marketing plans are of little value in day to day operations or for application to improvement activities. Similarly, operating plans that are merely financial plans provide insufficient information for aligning day to day operations.

There are some general concepts that apply to generating and deploying an enterprise Aim successfully.

1. The Aim should be created to endure. There is ample evidence that enterprises with an enduring Aim have a strategic advantage over those who do not. Enduring strategy is a key component to enduring profitability.

---

* For readers who would like to review the theory and application of developing an enterprise aim (strategic plan) may I recommend the following books: 1) *Built to Last*, James C. Collins and Jerry I. Porras, Harper-Collins, New York; 2) *The Fifth Discipline,* Peter M. Senge, Doubleday, New York; 3) *A New American TQM,* Shoji Shiba, et. al., Center for Quality Management, Productivity Press, Portland, OR.

2. The focus of the Aim should be on customer satisfaction and quality. Profits will follow.

3. The Aim should be created and executed with the idea of optimizing the enterprise system, not the individual components.

4. The Steering Committee must create a learning environment focused on customer satisfaction and continual improvement.

5. The Aim must be deployed to everyone to align the activities of people throughout the enterprise.

6. Development and deployment of a concise set of metrics will bring the plan to life and provide the means for everyone in the organization to understand how they may contribute to enterprise success.*

In deploying the Aim, it is important to realize that one time exposure accomplishes nothing. Managers at all levels should take each and every opportunity to "teach" the Aim (the purpose, goals, and values) to everyone in the organization.

In deploying the metrics, it is important to create visual references, often called "scoreboards." These scoreboards are usually located on a prominent wall (for instance, in the cafeteria) where everyone can see the metrics charts on a daily basis. Usually one or two key metrics are identified as critical indicators. Specific scoreboards for workgroups should be posted in the workspaces giving everyone immediate visual reference to how they are doing and how they are contributing to the enterprise Aim.

* For a review of creating a balanced set of metrics read "Putting the Balanced Scorecard to Work", Robert S. Kaplan and David P. Norton, Harvard Business Review, September-October 1993.

You should take great care in creating the format for displaying metrics. If you let installed office software do it, all your metrics charts will look just like all of your other charts, and people will likely say, "So what?" More dynamic and informative formats will utilize the *PPI* tools, primarily Pareto charts, run charts, process behavior charts, and histograms.* This will also reinforce the deployment and utilization of *PPI* methods.

Once the Aim (strategic guidance) and system of metrics are deployed a dedicated and deliberate effort must be made to align all improvement activities in the organization accordingly. Steering Committees at all levels should formally review metrics monthly, at a minimum. When appropriate, teams may be formed to address gaps, shortfalls, and problems.

## Identify Key Players

A viable support structure for *PPI* activities is crucial. There are several key positions within this structure. People should be selected for competence, ability, and reputation. If your good people are not in these positions, *PPI* deployment will be tentative. It is emphasized that *PPI* duties are conducted within the context of day to day work. *Do not hire additional people to administer the PPI program. PPI* contains the following organizational positions (a more complete description may be found in Chapter Seven).

---

* For information on constructing and using process behavior charts please read *Understanding Variation*, Donald J. Wheeler, SPC Press, Knoxville; *The New Economics*, Chapter 8-10, W. Edwards Deming, Massachusetts Institute of Technology, Cambridge. For information on use of basic tools please read *Guide to Quality Control*, Kaoru Ishikawa, JUSE Press Ltd, Tokyo distributed in North America by APO, Quality Resources, White Plains.

- A Program Champion: a senior manager in the organization, responsible for the success of the program
- A Program Coordinator: a manager responsible for day-to-day management of *PPI* activities (i.e., operations manager)
- A Program Administrator: responsible for schedules, administrative coordination, and materials
- Process Champions: assigned by the steering committee, responsible for the *PPI* teams' success and for implementation (Every manager in the enterprise is the Process Champion for teams improving their processes.)
- Facilitators: trained to *actively* engage the team and keep them on track
- *PPI* Teams: employee teams with projects derived from key business metrics, focused on the customer and employed to remove waste, save money, and improve profit
- Trainers: selected and trained to conduct the seminars during implementation: managers seminar, facilitators seminar, and team training (Outside resources may be required in the beginning with self sufficiency as soon as possible as the goal.)

In large enterprises there may be more than one level or layer of executive management. In that instance the position of Program Champion and Program Coordinator should be in place at each executive level where a Steering Committee has been formed.

## Create a Master Implementation Plan

As with any program, *PPI* will require a master plan for effective deployment. As Yogi Berra said, "You've got to be careful if you don't know where you're going 'cause you might not get there!"

The following steps are a guide to creating and deploying the master plan:

1. *Identify resources.*

   The key players—the Steering Committee, the Program Champion, and the Program Coordinator—are the people who develop the master plan. Logically, they should be selected and in place before deployment begins.

2. *Establish a time line and master schedule.*

   *PPI* will be deployed over time. The bottleneck is usually training. *PPI* training is conducted by first creating project teams and then training those teams as they complete their first projects. Teams are trained in groups of four or five teams containing between four and eight people each. Projects require six to twelve weeks for completion—usually twelve weeks in the beginning moving to six weeks as the program matures. Simple arithmetic will determine your deployment schedule based on training resources and availability of people.

3. *Coordinate and de-conflict other initiatives.*

   Normally, organizations embarking on a *PPI* initiative will be pursuing other initiatives as well. These initiatives may be unrelated, such as revamping the design process, departmental reorganizations, or physical plant moves or remodeling. There may be other quality and productivity initiatives as well, which may include ISO 9000 installation, audits, or updates, demand flow technology, and visual workplace programs. Opportunities for conflict should be carefully managed.

4. *Develop near-term and long-term training plans.*

   This step will be discussed in the next section

## Develop Near-Term and Long-Term Training Plans

The first step (a simple step that is often overlooked) is to create a master roster of everybody in the organization in spreadsheet format, displaying the various training that is required, by individual. It will then be a fairly simple matter of keeping track of who has had what training and who needs training.

Long term training plans should be created to provide an overall plan for training completion. Near term training plans should be created with specific dates and objectives. Assigning people to training randomly is to be avoided. People should be assigned to training *Just in Time* to fulfill their participation in their first team project.

There are four basic types of *PPI* training:

- **Managers Seminar:** This seminar, normally two days in length, is for managers at all levels in the organization. Participants will be taught the fundamentals of *PPI* as well as the structure, deployment requirements, and individual duties. Process champions must attend this seminar before participating in a team project.
- **Facilitators Seminar**: This seminar is designed to train people who have volunteered to be *PPI* facilitators. Normally four days in length, this seminar provides skills for *active* team facilitation. Participants will be taught their role and duties to actively keep the team engaged and moving toward their solutions. Facilitators must attend this seminar before participating in a team project.
- **Team Training:** As projects are identified and presented, all employees should attend this training. All members of a team participate in the same training at the same time. It

is highly desirable to train multiple teams simultaneously—usually betweenthree and five teams at a time. The training extends over the duration of the team project, six to twelve weeks. Employees never attend this seminar just to satisfy a training need. Teams are never formed just to satisfy a training need. The Steering Committee must carefully manage this training so that all employees attend as members of project teams working on meaningful and important problems. Facilitators attend all training and team meetings throughout the duration of the project. Process champions are required to attend as required to fulfill their duties. (Please refer back to Chapter Nine for more detail on conducting team training.)

- **Tool Experts**: There will be, from time to time, a need for advanced tools to complete a team's project or to fully implement potential solutions. Therefore, a small cadre trained in these advanced tools and methods may be required. In today's modern enterprises it is most likely that these tool experts are already available. So, before spending precious training dollars employees should be surveyed to find out what skills they possess. Areas to address include: advance planning and management tools, advanced facilitator's skills and tools, statistical process control and other statistical tools, ISO 9000, Advanced Product Quality Planning (APQP), design of industrial experiments (DOE), failure mode effects analysis (FMEA), and other advanced tools. This list is not exhaustive but is a good place to start. Many people have these skills but have never been asked to use them.

## Develop and Conduct *PPI* Projects

In developing and conducting *PPI* projects it is vital to remember that the objectives are customer satisfaction, improving quality, saving money, and improving profit. Team projects are not team-building exercises, nor are they simply the means to get people trained. Teams are not formed to meet quotas, nor are they formed around unimportant issues.

There are ten steps in developing and conducting *PPI* projects, each discussed below.

1. *Identify Problems from Key Business Metrics.*
   There are four requirements.
   - Team projects must be carefully chosen based on enterprise metrics. You may not always assign a team to the biggest problem for various reasons. But, you must assign teams only to important problems.
   - Teams must be assigned problems, never solutions. If you think you know the solution, just do it. Assigning a solution as a team project is always a disaster.
   - It is not appropriate to assign pre-determined financial goals to teams for they are self limiting. Cost savings are rolled up after the project is completed.
   - The focus is customer satisfaction. When focusing on customer satisfaction instead of dollar savings teams invariably surpass expectations.

2. *Balance Your Teams.*
   Ensure the team projects reflect a cross section of the organization. There is always a tendency to predominantly work on "operations" projects. Productivity and quality improvement is everybody's job.

3. *Assign a Process Champion who has knowledge and experience of the problem.*

   The Process Champion will be responsible for the team's success and will be responsible for implementing team solutions. It is preferable, therefore, to assign a manager from the functional area of the product or service being worked on. The Process Champion normally assigns team members.

4. *Select a Facilitator.*

   Facilitators are usually selected by the Process Champion but may be assigned by the Program Coordinator. Facilitators normally assist the Process Champion in selection of remaining team members.

5. *Select a Team Leader.*

   Team Leaders are responsible for administration of the team. They schedule meetings, arrange for meeting rooms, and fulfill other team management duties. They are the point of official communications for the team. It is usually helpful to assign a Team Leader who has seniority and natural leadership abilities.

6. *Carefully assign project team members.*

   Team members must be assigned for the knowledge, skills, and ability to analyze and solve the problem at hand. This means, among other things, team members should have knowledge of the product or service being worked on. There might be a rare occasion when unassociated people may serve on teams but these assignments should be managed carefully.

7. *Schedule training.*

   Ensure all resources are lined up to support the training portions of the team project. Selection of a training site is very important. Several teams should undergo training at the same time to create a situation where they can learn from each other and share best practices. Arrangements should be made for break out rooms for selected portions of the training.

8. *Conduct the project.*
   Projects normally last six to twelve weeks. There will be seven formal training meetings and usually one or two 2-hour meetings in-between the training meetings. If the training meetings are scheduled weekly the project will be six weeks. If the training meetings are scheduled every other week the project will be twelve weeks. The first two training meetings are in the first week and are each a full day in duration. The third training meeting is in the second or third week (depending if the training meetings are every week or every other week) and will be a full day. The following training meetings will be one-half day duration. Teams will follow The Eight Step Method in completing their projects (Chapter Eight has more details on rules for conducting projects using The Eight Step Method).

9. *Conduct formal "Report-Outs".*
   At the end of the six or twelve week project cycle, teams will be scheduled for a formal Report-Out. The Report-Out milestone, among other things, provides a stretch goal (facilitating anxiety) which helps motivation. Normally teams will have decided upon and tested their solutions by report out and may even have begun some implementation activities. It is rare that teams have not reached at least some solutions by time of Report-Out. Sometimes the teams may have reached solutions but have not completed the testing. Regardless, it is important that teams "Report-Out" on time. They will be required to prepare and present

an implementation and control plan that lists by date, responsibility, and activity all actions required to complete the project. It will be the Process Champion's responsibility to make sure the team completes the project fully including all actions required by the implementation and control plan.

10. *Hold the gains and track project metrics.*
    The Process Champion will be specifically responsible for ensuring that all actions required in the implementation and control plan are completed. In addition to team members people outside of the team are assigned actions as required.

The measure of team success is the team output metric chart. The output metric derives directly from the team goal. It is presented in the form of a run chart or a process behavior chart showing progress over time. The Process Champion and Team Leader maintain these charts for at least six months. The Steering Committee reviews the output metrics from active teams at least monthly. The Steering Committee decides when the output metric indicates success – from that point maintenance of the chart is at the discretion of the Process Champion.

## Create Processes for Ongoing Success

At Report-Out, teams will present a list of future actions (Step Eight of The Eight Step Method is reserved for determining future plans). These future actions take the following form:

- Future action of the team. The team may recommend that they not disband at the end of their project but, rather, continue to work on similar problems in associated products or services. Or, they might want to go another round on the same project in order to meet, for example, a customer requirement.

- Problems uncovered by the team that are outside the team's boundaries or beyond the team's ability to take appropriate action. These should be addressed by the Steering Committee with creation of appropriate action items.

- It is important that a process is in place to track these future actions. Establishing and maintaining this process will be the responsibility of the Program Coordinator.

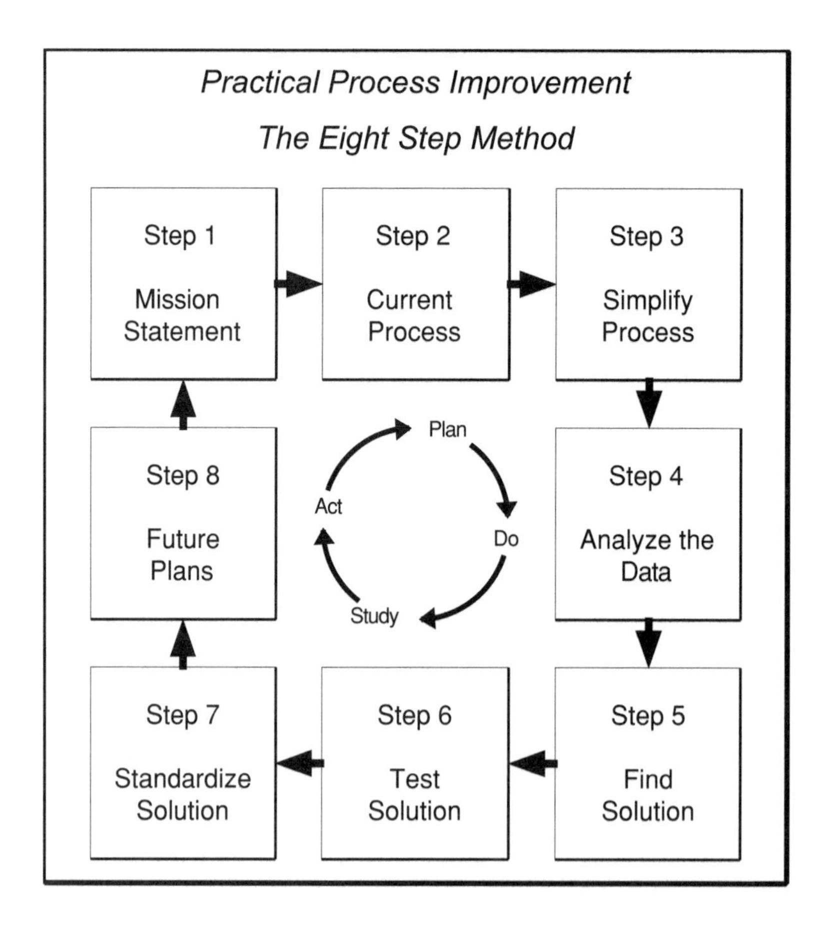

Finally, senior managers should recognize that, like any other program, *PPI* will require a certain level of marketing effort to be successful. Team successes should be publicized. Periodically, the Program Coordinator and a finance manager should roll up dollar savings from *PPI* projects. Efforts to market *PPI* should appropriately be integrated with efforts to deploy the enterprise Aim and system of metrics.

## Summary

So, let's summarize briefly what we have discussed. We introduced this book by stating that Practical Process Improvement is a simple approach to making money by involving everyone in the enterprise. There is a common objective: *to boost profit* by practical application of proven methods.

*PPI* operates on two paths simultaneously. First, we accrue savings from waste reduction and process improvement. Second, we increase revenue by improving customer satisfaction with our products and services. We leverage the combined effect of these two paths to maximize enterprise effectiveness and profitability.

*PPI* employs three principles: 1) apply logical simplicity, 2) use practical methods and tools, and 3) involve everyone. *PPI* is employed by everyone in the organization, not only by an anointed cadre of "experts" who reserve knowledge and authority to their exclusive domain.

The primary focus of *PPI* is customer satisfaction. This focus requires alignment of all activities with a view to satisfying the customer now and in the future. Our customer focus requires that we be innovative and forward looking.

Customer satisfaction is measurable within the following elements or dimensions:

- Quality
- Delivery
- Price
- Image
- Anticipation (future requirements).

We discussed the application of two production methods toward the end of customer satisfaction—the detection method and the prevention method. The detection method relies on 100% screening inspection to ensure only good product is shipped to the customer. This method does nothing to improve product quality, it only sorts product to specification. The detection method is costly.

The prevention method improves customer satisfaction by improving product quality. Quality is improved by improving the processes of production which has the added effect of reducing operating costs. While quality and customer satisfaction are improved, resulting in increasing revenues, production costs are reduced. This two path approach, applied within the *PPI* program, accelerates profitable growth.

*PPI* employs some simple and powerful basic tools and statistical tools. The most powerful and descriptive tool is the process behavior chart. This chart operationally defines our processes, provides a reasonable prediction of future process performance, and takes the guesswork out of what sort of process improvement is required.

We provided ten Guidelines for Success. These Guidelines provide practical and usable rules and strategies for employment in formal process improvement efforts and everyday work. We also discussed the necessity for management involvement in order for the *PPI* program to be successful.

The Guidelines for Success are a good start for managers desiring to increase their involvement.

In Part Two we discussed some of the more mundane aspects of the *PPI* program including the organization and support system, the *PPI* team model, and the training process. Finally, we provided some hands on guidance for getting started on the *PPI* journey. We hope this book has encouraged you embark on this journey.

Remember, it does not matter when you begin as long as you start now.

# Avoiding Sigma Confusion

by Donald J. Wheeler

It is important, in any improvement effort, to distinguish between the *Voice of the Customer*, which is commonly expressed in specification limits, and what Bill Scherkenbach called the *Voice of the Process*. The Voice of the Customer defines what you want to deliver. The Voice of the Process defines what you are going to obtain from your system of production. Since your job is to make sure that these two voices are in alignment, it is critical that you do not confuse the two.

Process behavior charts define the Voice of the Process. Specifically, they do this by means of the Natural Process Limits, which are defined as symmetric, three-sigma limits for individual values. The Natural Process Limits not only define the routine variation you can expect from a predictable process, but they also approximate the process potential for an unpredictable process. As will be shown in the next section, these symmetric, three-sigma limits are sufficiently general to work with virtually every type of process. Thus, when talking about the Voice of the Process, we use three-sigma limits.

So why do you hear the term "six sigma" today? While there are many different programs that are collectively referred under the banner of six sigma, the only thing they all have in common is that they have adopted the language of *process* variation to describe the Voice of the Customer.

Traditionally the Voice of the Customer was defined by the specification limits and the difference in these specification limits known as the specified tolerance. Now, the various six sigma programs express the specified tolerance in terms of the units of variation in the production process (sigma units rather than measurement units). Thus, when someone says that they want to have a six sigma process, they are simply saying that they would like for the specification limits to be plus or minus six sigma units on either side of the process average (a specified tolerance of twelve sigma units). This would correspond to a Capability Ratio of 2.0, and would look something like the following figure.

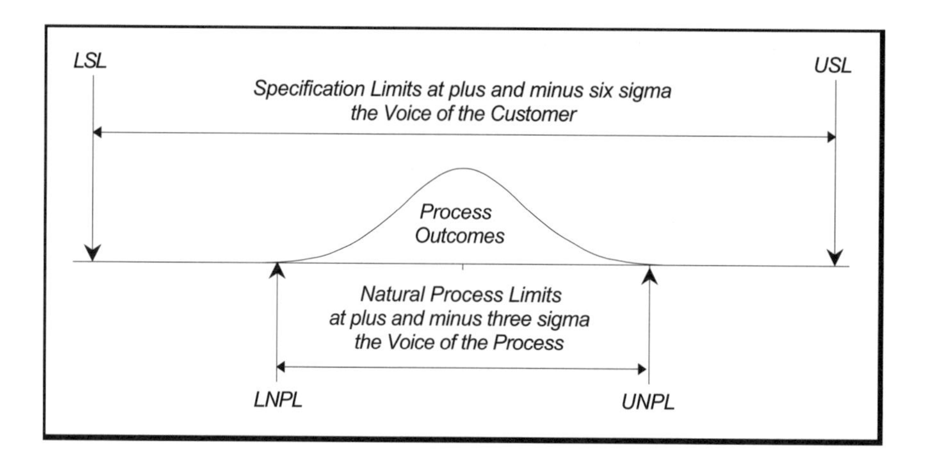


Since, as we will see in a moment, no process needs more than plus or minus three sigma units of elbow room, having specifications at plus or minus six sigma units will result in a considerable operational cushion. This will be, in general, very desirable.

Thus, by using the language of process variation to describe the specified tolerance, the six sigma programs have created some confusion. The Voice of the Process is defined by symmetric, three-sigma limits. We would like to have the Voice of the Customer defined by symmetric six-sigma specifications. Without a clear distinction between these two voices confusion is inevitable.

Moreover, since there are two voices, there are two completely different ways of getting a "six-sigma process." You could set the specifications where they need to be and reduce the process variation to the point that you will have a Capability Ratio of $C_p = 2.0$, or you could measure the variation in the process outcomes and change the specifications to give $C_p = 2.0$. The first approach maintains design integrity while it improves both product quality and customer satisfaction. The second approach does none of these things—but since it does deliver the right number, it will provide a false and fleeting sense of well-being.

## How Symmetric Three-Sigma Limits Work

Many students of statistics have learned how to compute various measures of dispersion, such as the standard deviation statistic, *s*, without ever learning what these measures do. In effect, when we compute a standard measure of dispersion, we are obtaining a conversion factor that expresses the number of measurement units that correspond to one standard unit of dispersion.

Once we know the size of a standard unit of dispersion there are certain things we can say with complete generality. In order to illustrate these generalities, we will use six probability models. Each of these models will be shown in their standardized form, where their mean is 0 and their standard deviation parameter is exactly 1. The generalities these models will illustrate are commonly referred to as the three Empirical Rules.

**Empirical Rule One:** The bulk of a probability model will be contained within the interval defined by:

[ Mean ± One Standard Deviation ]

As can be seen in the following figures, most probability models will have between 60% to 75% of the area under the curve within the interval above.

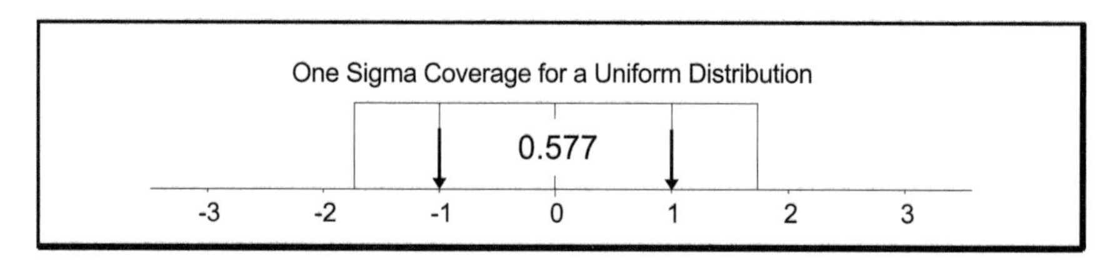


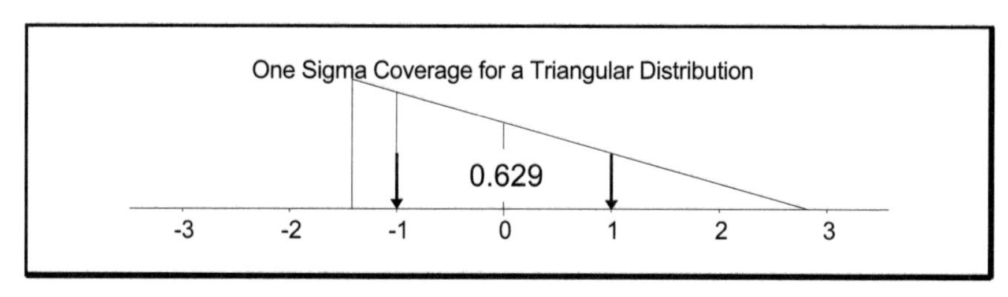


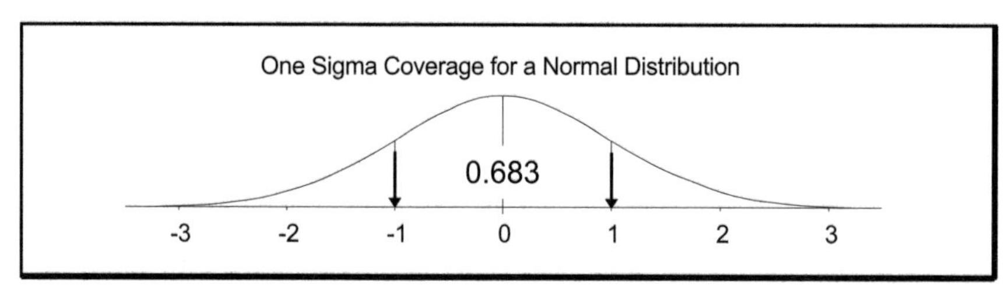

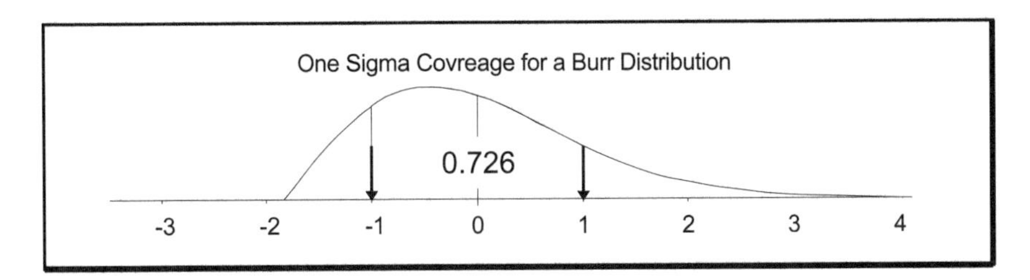


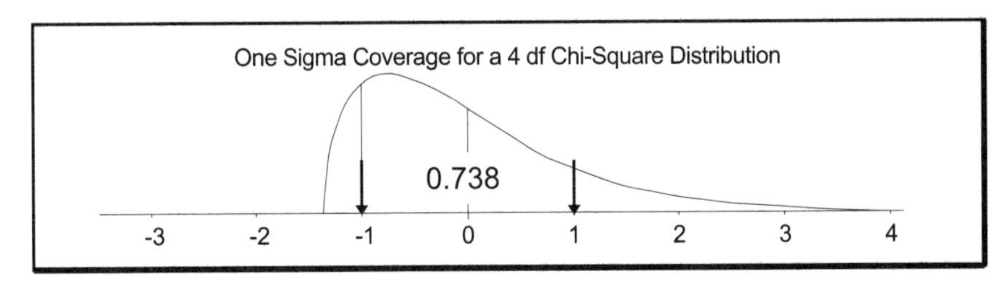


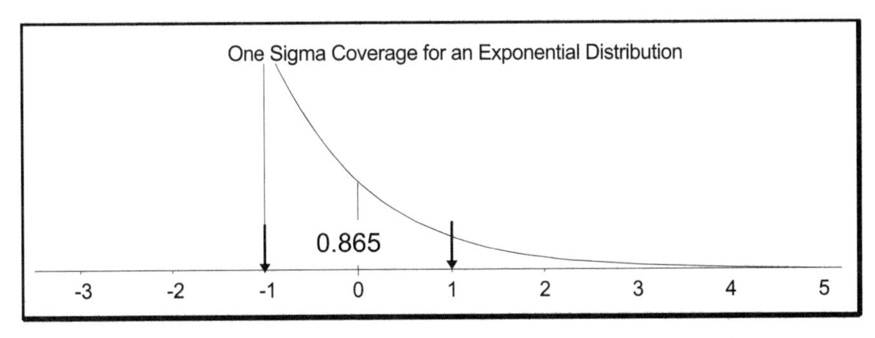


In general terms, we could say that roughly two-thirds of the probability will be found within one standard deviation unit of the mean.

**Empirical Rule Two:** Usually at least 90% of a probability model will be contained within the interval defined by:

[ Mean ± Two Standard Deviations ]

As can be seen in the following figures, all the models satisfy this rule. In general we expect around 95% of the probability to be found within two standard deviations of the mean.

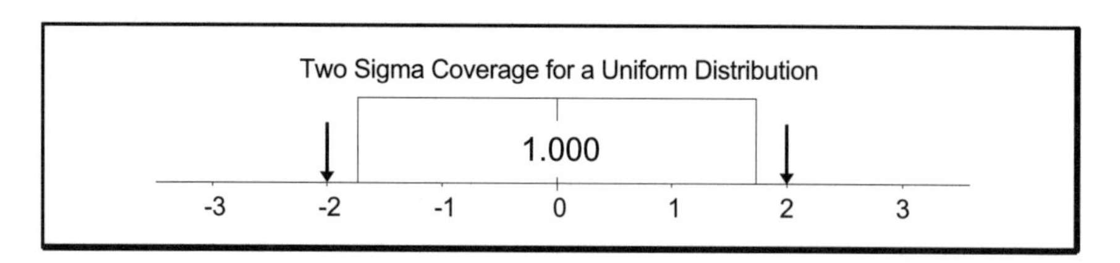
Two Sigma Coverage for a Uniform Distribution
1.000
-3
-2
-1
0
1
2
3

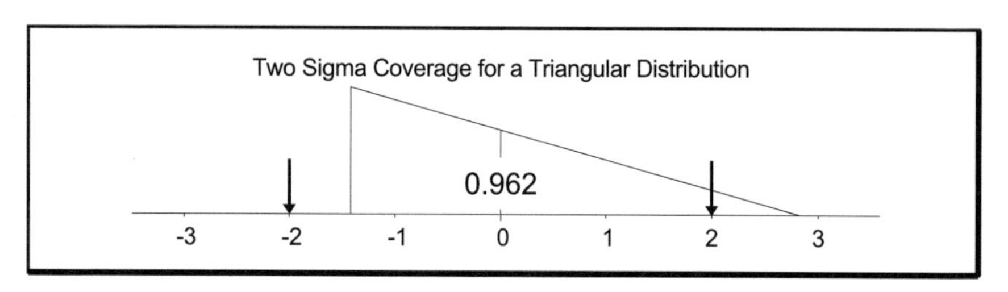
Two Sigma Coverage for a Triangular Distribution
0.962
-3
-2
-1
0
1
2
3

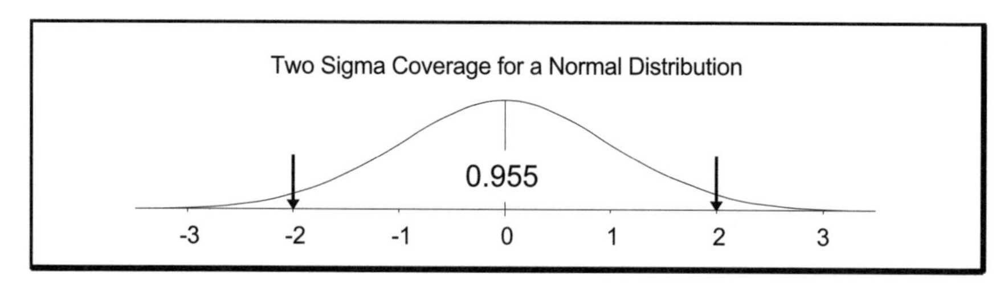
Two Sigma Coverage for a Normal Distribution
0.955
-3
-2
-1
0
1
2
3

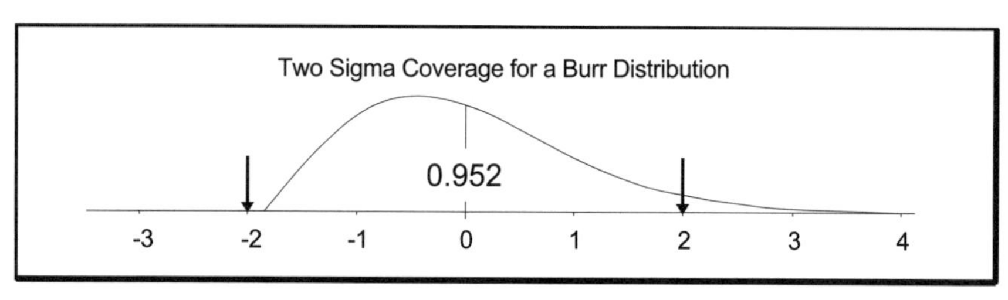
Two Sigma Coverage for a Burr Distribution
0.952
-3
-2
-1
0
1
2
3
4

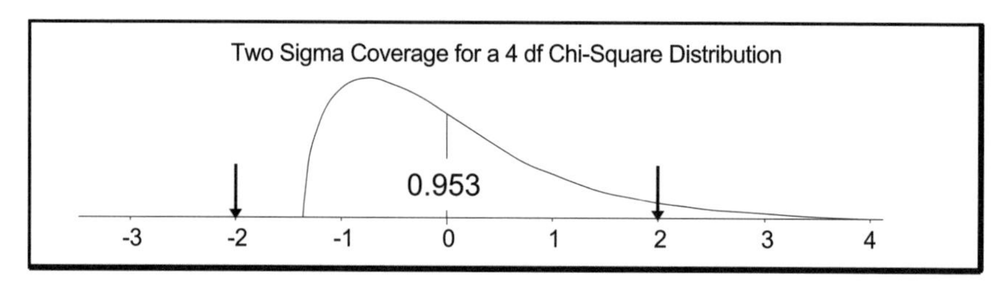
Two Sigma Coverage for a 4 df Chi-Square Distribution
0.953
-3
-2
-1
0
1
2
3
4

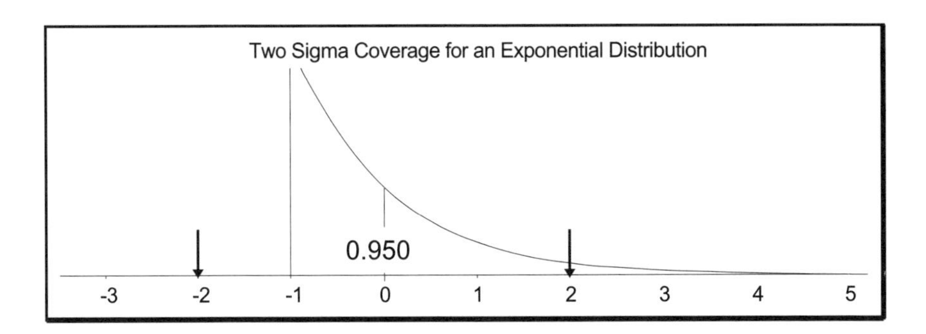


**Empirical Rule Three:** Approximately 99% to 100% of a probability model will be contained within the interval defined by:

[ Mean ± Three Standard Deviations ]

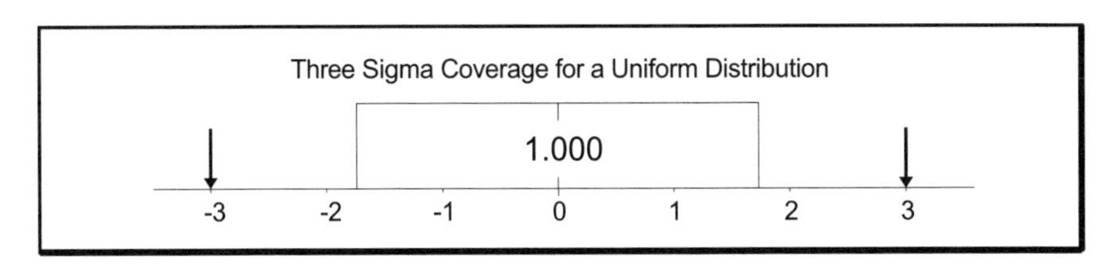


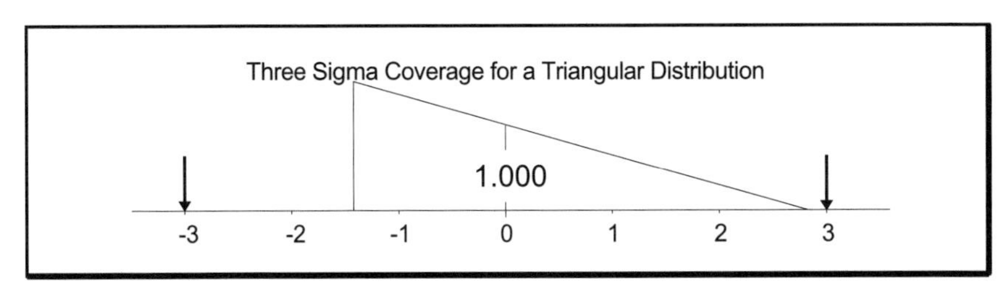


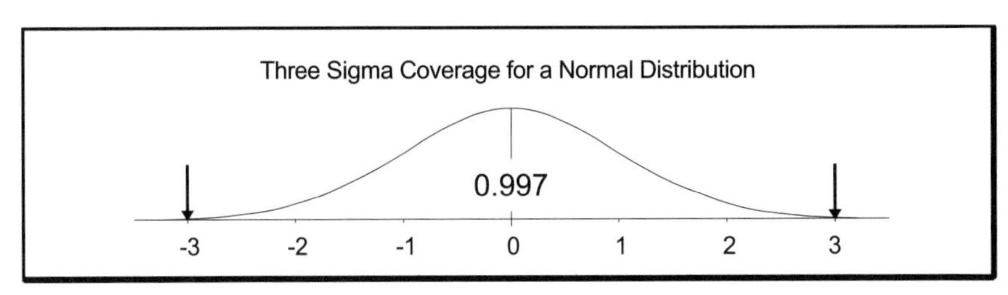

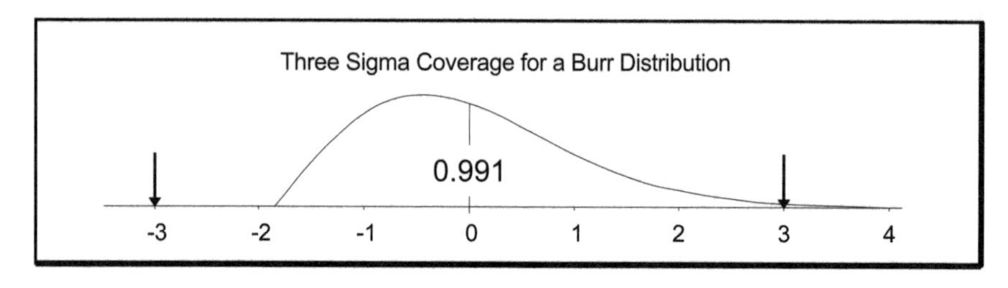


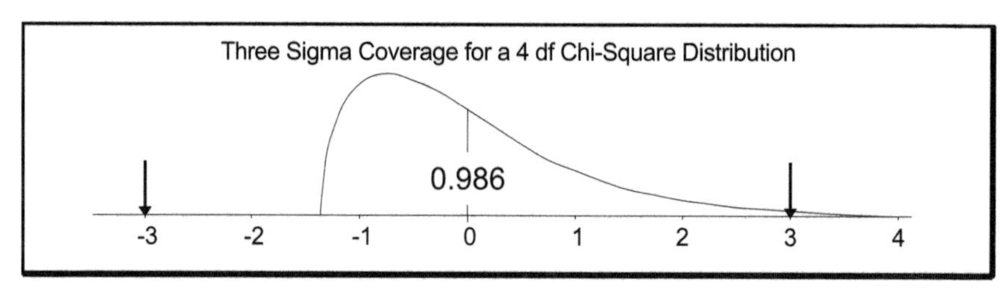


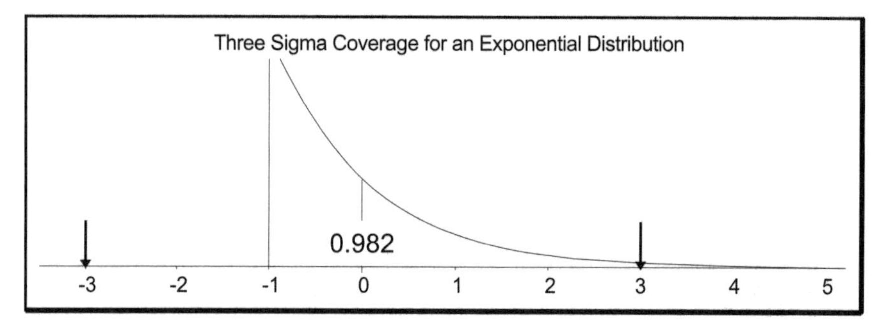


Mound-shaped and all but the most extreme of the J-shaped probability models will have virtually all of their probability within three standard deviations of the mean.

Thus, in terms of what you can expect from a predictable process, symmetric three-sigma limits will be sufficient to define the bounds of routine variation. Occasionally an isolated point might fall just outside these limits, but to describe the routine outcomes it is not necessary to go beyond three-sigma limits.

This general property of three-sigma limits removes the necessity of having to determine just which probability model might describe our process outcomes, and thereby greatly simplifies the whole approach to data analysis.

So three-sigma limits may be used to define the Voice of the Process. At the same time, since we will still want to have an operational cushion, we will want to have *specifications* that are outside the Natural Process Limits. Thus, we like to have specifications that are four-sigma, five-sigma, and six-sigma on either side of the process average.

## How to Compute Sigma

Since process behavior charts are used to separate the routine variation from any exceptional variation that may be present in the data, there are certain ways in which we *must* compute the value for sigma. (This also implies, necessarily, that there are incorrect ways of computing sigma for the purposes of a process behavior chart.)

In order to separate the routine variation from any exceptional variation that may be present, limits on a process behavior chart must always be computed using the average of multiple local measures of dispersion. In other words, our value for *Sigma(X)* must have one of the following forms or an equivalent form:

$$Sigma(X) = \frac{\bar{R}}{d_2}$$

$$Sigma(X) = \frac{\bar{s}}{c_4}$$

$$Sigma(X) = \frac{\tilde{R}}{d_4}$$

$$Sigma(X) = \frac{\bar{s}_n}{c_2}$$

where $c_2$, $c_4$, $d_2$, and $d_4$ are the appropriate bias correction factors tabled in most books on SPC.

Specifically, when computing limits for a process behavior chart, you cannot use a standard deviation statistic, $s$, that has been computed globally (using all the data at once).

Do not let the use of the terms three sigma and six sigma lull you into thinking that you know what is being discussed. Until you have studied from a reputable text you can easily get into trouble. There are over 50 ways to compute measures of dispersion and they are not all equivalent from the perspective of data analysis. The right ways are easy to use, but so are the wrong ways. Therefore you need to know the difference in order to avoid making a serious mistake.

## Recommended Reading

More information on the logic, construction, and use of process behavior charts can be found in the following books:

*Understanding Variation: the Key to Managing Chaos*
by Donald J. Wheeler,

*Making Sense of Data: SPC for the Service Sector*
by Donald J. Wheeler,

*Understanding Statistical Process Control, Second Edition*
by Donald J. Wheeler and David S. Chambers.

These titles are available from SPC Press at spcpress.com.